Play for Convalescent Children

Play for Convalescent Children

Play for Convalescent Children

in hospitals and at home

Revised Edition

by

Anne Marie Smith

New York • A. S. BARNES AND COMPANY, INC.

London • THOMAS YOSELOFF LTD.

A. S. Barnes and Company, Inc.
11 East 36th Street
New York 16, N. Y.

Thomas Yoseloff Ltd.
123 New Bond Street
London, W.1, England

PRINTED IN THE UNITED STATES OF AMERICA

C813390

TO

NEVA L. BOYD

PREFACE TO THE SECOND EDITION

The need for written material on play with small children in clinics and hospitals is a real one. It is gratifying to have such a need met in this book. Miss Anne Smith, with her vast experience, is an authority in this field and shares her wit, knowledge, and know-how with all prospective "play ladies."

Most children are apprehensive and fearful when they come to a clinic or hospital. This insecurity often produces a crying and uncooperative patient. It might result in a life-long fear of going to the doctor. On the other hand, an excited youngster releases his emotions and excess energy through noise and turmoil. Both behaviors result in confusion during the clinic session.

These problems can be solved by a warm "play lady." Through play on the child's level, she gains his confidence and makes him less insecure. A clinic visit can even become fun for him. The excited rambunctious youngster finds outlets for energy through constructive and organized play. As one mother said, "The atmosphere in the clinics since play was introduced has been so relaxed." According to the clinic nurses, "The children find the play lady very entertaining. They play quietly and enjoy their clinic visit. This helps the staff run a better clinic," "I have found Miss Smith most fascinating and interesting. She has taught the nurses and mothers many interesting and simple games that can be made out of household items that anyone has around the house." The doctor finds the child happy and more cooperative when it is time to examine him.

The purpose of play in clinics and hospitals, therefore, is to dispel fear among the children and to provide a more relaxed atmosphere.

EVELYN E. HARTMAN, M.D.
Director, Maternal and Child Health
Minneapolis Health Department

PREFACE TO THE FIRST EDITION

The child's psychological needs are the same whether he is sick or well. In addition to medical treatment the hospitalized child needs love and security; interesting, satisfying and instructive activity; satisfying social relationships and responsibility; and release from emotional tensions. Psychologists tell us that if these needs are not satisfied, the child will develop behavior disorders.

Miss Smith has portrayed graphically the well-rounded play program carried on at The Children's Memorial Hospital where such a program has proved practical, and is regarded as essential to the mental and emotional health of the hospitalized child.

The majority of our patients on the average pediatric ward are convalescing from upper respiratory infections, fractures, hernias, appendectomies, burns, and after a very few days they are bubbling over with energy that must have an outlet.

The following are some of the benefits of play as observed in our pediatric ward: Proper play brings relaxation and induces the rest that is necessary in the care and treatment of the sick child. It brings immediate satisfaction to the child and he is free from the strain that so often results from school work. A story, game, or song diverts the child's mind from the mental and emotional stress and the depleting effects of pain and thereby conserves his energy for the regaining of physical health. Play also prevents crying spells due to homesickness and other less obvious causes. An adequate play program together with the policy of never lying to the children does much to prevent the development of unnecessary fears that might leave "psychological scars." In dealing with the fears, angers and resentments that seem almost unavoidable, play becomes a wholesome safeguard. Play fosters good habits of the constructive use of the child's energy, and these habits prevent less desirable ones as thumb sucking, nail biting, masturbation and others.

In regard to equipping nurses with education in play for children it may be said that play creates new relationships between the nurse and the child and destroys any fear they may have of each other. Doctors also find that play establishes happy relationships with the child. I recall a young doctor examining a frightened, screaming child. He said, "Let's play telephone." He used the stethoscope for a telephone and immediately had a coöperative child.

Parents have more confidence in the hospital staff when they see that the doctors and nurses understand and are bent upon making the children happy as well as on giving them their best medical treatment.

(Mrs.) MILDRED MCCULLOUGH
Supervising Instructor in Pediatric Nursing,
San Francisco City and County Hospital

AUTHOR'S FOREWORD
TO THE SECOND EDITION

We live in an exciting period which many claim is the beginning of a new era that requires better methods for wholesome human development. For research has made great strides forward, as dramatic in exploring human beings —though not as much before the public eye—as man's efforts to reach the planets. New methods are changing practice not only in home life and hospitals but in social, business, and other relations. Research—during, between, and after three wars—is modifying and often completely reversing earlier beliefs and methods. Now, play is a long way from being "just kid stuff," children merely miniature adults, and leisure "the Devil's handiwork." Consensus in various fields claims the foundations of personality are laid in infancy. The emotional patterns social attitudes, and goals from early childhood through adulthood are started then, and play by baby and mother—or her substitute—is considered one of the most important elements in that foundation.

The last forty years produced a flood of books on human development and on the many types of play activities. Only a few of the main factors that produced these changes can be traced within the scope of this book, but even a bird's-eye view may help the reader better to understand present conditions. In the midst of contradictions between old and new ideas it helps to see our jobs in relation to the events that brought about these changes in values, and to look back even further to the older promoters of play.

In this new profession of play or recreation leader—or therapist in hospitals and clinics—specialization in one field of play or on one developmental tends to limit a person's viewpoint and the results of his work. Those dealing with adults may find they understand the adults better and can give them more help in developing their potentialities, even in cases of mental disturbance; such persons often are still children who haven't grown up.

A section on play in clinics has been added, based on experience in three Minneapolis Public Health Clinics and Kenny Institute. Tested play activities are described along with methods that proved helpful to the volunteers, the mothers and students doing field work. Because many are at a loss on how to proceed without a lot of toys and other material equipment, emphasis was on social types of play and on the use of scrap materials that appeal to a child's imagination. Our thanks are extended to the ladies of Jones-Harrison Home, to the Universalist Women's Service Group, Camp Fire Girls, and Girl Scouts who contributed materials and finished play equipment based on this experiment.

To Dr. Evelyn E. Hartman and Mrs. Lena Berg, who made this experiment possible, to the Minnesota University Press for permission to use the quotation from *Child Care and Training* by Faegre, Anderson, and Harris, to Mrs. Vera Flandorf for her list of books on Helping the Child to Adjust to the Hospital Situation, and to the volunteers who helped with play in clinics, I extend heartiest thanks.

Minneapolis, Minnesota
1960   A. M. S.

AUTHOR'S FOREWORD
TO THE FIRST EDITION

Over a million children are admitted every year to hospitals in the United States where it is estimated that forty per cent of the child's day is taken up by physical care. How one hospital uses play, the "child's language," to help fill in a constructive way that sixty per cent of time left over after physical care has been attended to is told here.

This book is an account of approximately six years of experimenting with play for the children under treatment at The Children's Memorial Hospital in Chicago and in the education of the nurses receiving their pediatric training there. The hospital had a capacity of 252 beds and treated approximately 4,000 patients annually. In its School of Pediatric Nursing, 1,004 student nurses from affiliated hospitals and 77 graduate nurses were given courses in play during the period 1932 to 1938 as a fundamental method for their understanding care of children.

Among the questions which this experiment sought to answer were: What can be done with a full-time, integrated program of play in a children's hospital? Will children respond favorably or are they too ill to care to play? In what situations is group play useful? Will play make the children any happier and more contented than they are without it? Is play a vital factor in the care and treatment of children? Can the nurse's ability to understand and deal with children be increased by a short course in play?

The conclusions reached are not those of one person. Records reveal the attitudes and viewpoints of the hospital administrators and nurses, and the spontaneous expressions of parents and visitors regarding play as it was tried out in various hospital situations.

By the end of the period so many records had accumulated in answer to these questions, the idea of embodying them in a book took shape. The book is intended for those interested in the welfare of children. Parents, psychiatrists, psychologists, and the general public may be interested in learning what play has accomplished in changing children's fears of hospitals and in giving them greater confidence in the physicians and nurses. Administrators and physicians in children's hospitals and those responsible for the education of pediatric nurses may find in these pages suggestions that, carried out in nursing education and in the treatment of children, contribute to making hospital experience happier and more constructive.

Although this book deals with the child in the hospital situation, the activities, the principles, the values of play and of group methods are applicable to children anywhere. Universities and other schools may find the theories of group play helpful in giving students a clearer understanding of child behavior, not only in hospitals, but in homes, schools, institutions and camps.

The writer extends grateful acknowledgment to the Board Members of The Children's Memorial Hospital of Chicago who made possible this experiment with play with the children and nurses in the hospital; to Neva L. Boyd of Northwestern University and the Northwestern University students who, under her supervision, did the initial work which led to a full-time program; to the nurses and volunteer workers who helped to make play an accepted part of hospital care; and to the physicians and administrators who coöperated in this new experiment.

To Alexis Carrel, Herbert S. Jennings, Harold H. Anderson, Edward A. Strecker, Willem van de Wall, Winifred Rand, Elizabeth Lee Vincent, Neva L. Boyd, and Agatha Shea for their gracious permission to use extracts from their writings, to Harper and Brothers for permission to use the selection from *Man, The Unknown,* by Alexis Carrel, to Gertrude Tait, Maren Elwood, Neva L. Boyd and the publishers for their helpful criticism in the preparation of the manuscript, the writer is most grateful.

A.M.S.

Chicago, Illinois

1941

INTRODUCTION

Hospital administrators who accept the findings of modern science to the effect that the physical, mental, and emotional aspects of human beings are inseparable are not satisfied with providing patients with physical care alone. Treatment involves the total personality.

Progressive boards of directors and administrators of pediatric hospitals realize also that the child must be viewed not only in the immediate hospital environment but in relation to his future life in the community. Leading toward that end, a wider horizon opens, a broader field of treatment. The child is not only a sick child. He is a human being with potentialities ripe for development, and whether in a hospital or elsewhere, just because he is a child, he is dependent upon adults to provide the environment in which he may develop. Such an environment must for a child include play.

But faulty conceptions of play have too often resulted in inadequate provision for the many-sided needs of children in institutions. Regarding play as merely an amusement or diversion, moving pictures, puppet shows, and other entertainment are occasionally provided by persons from outside the hospital. Add to this the listening to the radio and the patients are largely confined to passive participation. Play for the hospitalized children is often looked upon as a means of keeping them quiet and giving an orderly appearance

17

to the wards. In some institutions the teaching of arts, crafts, nature study, and the like is considered to constitute the whole of play. Psychiatrists frequently use specific types of play materials as an aid in diagnosing problem behavior. In some hospitals play utilized in the treatment becomes play therapy. From this atomistic conception of play comes the request for classifications of games to be used in cases of different diseases. The mental hygienists urge play as a prevention of neurotic conditions.

But there are still others who consider play, like food and rest, important to the mental, social, emotional, and ethical development of all children. In this sense it may be thought of as therapeutic.

Potentially, play holds all these values but they will not be actualized if play is treated piecemeal, or otherwise distorted by the failure to realize that, sick or well, we are all dealing with the whole child.

Experience at The Children's Memorial Hospital in Chicago demonstrates how effective play can be when organized as an integral part of the hospital care of children and as a fundamental part of the education of pediatric nurses. This book gives an account of the organization and administration of an experimental program of play as it functioned throughout the hospital and immediately before operations. It discusses the effectiveness of play as therapy for children and compares it with other forms of therapy and other systems. It also deals with the reactions of the children, the nurses, the parents and the visitors to play and discusses its influence in bringing about greater harmony, better cooperation, and on the part of the parents and children, a sense of security and confidence in the hospital staff. It offers evidence that the child absorbed in play has neither time nor reason to become habituated to invalidism. The effectiveness of play is shown in the education of the child as a means of developing his potentialities.

The methods of using play in instructing nurses, volunteer workers, parents and visitors are shown. Excerpts from the nurses' own records reveal that courses in play and the experience of playing with children on the wards and in the dispensary gave them new incentives and assurance of success in their care of the children and in their contacts with the parents.

CONTENTS

Play for Convalescent Children

Play for Convalescent Children

CHAPTER I

NEW ATTITUDES IN USING PLAY

THE TREATMENT OF THE WHOLE CHILD IN THE HOSPITAL SITUA-
TION. Revaluations of aims, methods, and results in the care
of the child seem characteristic of our times. With the attention of whole nations directed, particularly since the
World War, toward the best means of conservation and care
of children, hospitals and other institutions are analyzing existing conditions. They have a share in fulfilling at least two
of the objectives stated in the Children's Charter by the
White House Conference of 1930:

II. For every child, understanding and the guarding of his
personality as his most precious right.

VI. For every child from birth through adolescence, promotion
of health, including health instruction and a health program,
wholesome physical and mental recreation, with teachers and
leaders adequately trained.

Not so many years ago, those in charge of children's hospitals thought they had discharged their entire duty when
they had treated a patient expertly for his disease. Today,
in the light of scientific discovery in regard to what affects
the well-being of children, no modern, progressive admin-
istrator of a hospital for children can accept such a view.
Scientific research during the past thirty years has revealed
that the physical, mental, and emotional aspects of every
human being are inseparable. In the medical field it is recognized that disease may be an expression of emotional dis-

turbance or vice versa and also that a large percentage of patients have no organic disease. The following statement by authorities in different fields sustains this point of view. Dr. Strecker claims:

"It is not an overstatement to say that fully fifty per cent of the acute stages of an illness and seventy-five per cent of the difficulties of convalescence have their primary origin not in the body but in the mind of the patient." [1]

Both Miss Rand and Miss Vincent, who have devoted years to the study of children, express this point of view in discussing the hospital care of children.

"It is utterly ridiculous to be concerned for a healthy body, without consideration for the health of the personality or for the health of the personality without concern for the health of the body, as if you attempted to care for a child one day and neglected it the next. What would you say, for example, to a person whom you criticized for neglecting a child, if she replied, "Well, I fed him yesterday." So our emphasis on one aspect and our neglect of another aspect of child care is ridiculous. It is as lopsided for a hospital to give exquisite physical care and pay no attention to the other aspects of a child's needs as if we fed him one day and neglected him the next. If the hospital is going to have this all-round point of view of health, it is going to affect its attitude in regard to the responsibility it has toward the patient's future, and if that patient is a child, that means that the hospital has a responsibility toward the parents because the child's future is bound up in the parent. The hospital then is going to embark on a teaching program for the parent. It is going to teach something of the care of children in its broad sense, and not limit itself to physical considerations alone." [2]

1. Strecker, E. A., "Mental Hygiene," *Loose-Leaf Living Medicine,* Vol. VII, p. 413, New York, Nelson (1928).
2. Rand, Winifred, "Opportunities for Parent Education in the Children's Hospital and Means for Developing Them." *Hospitals, The Journal of the American Hospital Association,* Vol. X, p. 51 (December, 1936).

Miss Vincent claims:

"There are some things that are unquestionably well established. One is that sick children have a lower threshold of pain, of fatigue, of fear than well children. By a lower threshold I mean that they are more susceptible. It takes less pain to make them feel it, less fear to make them terrorized, less insecurity to make them afraid than well children."

She pointed out that the emergency conditions under which a very large proportion of children are brought into a hospital cause acute emotional conditioning:

"The stage is set under the conditions for a vivid, permanent impression on the child's learning, on his mental state, and his emotional habits. That means that we must not be just ordinarily concerned with the impressions and experiences that these children have. We must be vitally concerned since we realize that what happens to these children under these dramatic conditions does actually—we have proved it repeatedly, there is no question about it—remain as an impression more permanently in their personal and physiological equipment than ordinary experiences. That means, then, if we allow needless terror to occur, if we deceive them, we are making an impression on those youngsters that will remain perhaps for years." [3]

Such responsibility has been accepted for years by The Children's Memorial Hospital of Chicago. The human side of a hospital has long been stressed in word and deed by the physician-in-chief. The reasons for the hospital policies were summed up by the superintendent, who stated in substance that dreadful things could be done to a child even during a twenty-four-hour stay in a hospital, and that his

3. Vincent, Elizabeth Lee, "The Human Side of a Children's Hospital," *Hospitals, The Journal of the American Hospital Association*, Vol. XI, pp. 130-131 (January, 1937).
(Note: For proof of this evidence she refers to H. Flanders Dunbar's *Emotions and Bodily Change,* a résumé of the research that has been done the last thirty years.)

entire outlook on life can be changed for better or worse during a period of several months. Because children are developing rapidly during this formative period of early childhood, each day brings changes in them. For the child in a hospital Miss Binner advocates a day as nearly as possible like that of a normally well child.[4]

PLAY SERVES AS "PREVENTIVE MEDICINE." A child newly admitted to a hospital is like a stranger in a foreign land who knows little or nothing of the language. The worries of his parents, that are so easily apprehended by the child, exaggerate whatever feeling of insecurity or dread he may have when placed in a situation so different from anything he has experienced before. These fears are intensified by his own lack of time sense when separated from his parents. Moreover, detrimental habits are easily formed when there is little to occupy him but himself and this strange environment.

To the sensitive, the cumulative effects of envisioning a large hospital filled with the sick and suffering may be so overpowering as to produce lasting psychological effects. Consequently, since morbid influences affect the child more forcefully during illness than in health, how important it is that in the child's first realization of illness and death, shock be avoided, suffering be alleviated and environment be conducive to cheerfulness and courage in facing the problems he has to meet!

One may accept the belief that childhood illnesses, or the environment during illness, are frequently the initial cause of mental difficulties or he may incline toward Dr. Adler's view that they serve only as "the occasions that bring

4. Binner, Mabel W., "They Play with You Here." *The Modern Hospital*, Vol. 44, p. 57 (February, 1935), St. Louis, The Modern Hospital Pub. Co.

out hidden character flaws in the child."[5] In any case the fact remains that during childhood illnesses, such tendencies are revealed and can be so treated as to benefit the child and thereby lessen the dangers of later mental disturbance. Dr. Carrel sounds a warning regarding the dangers of mental and nervous disorders:

"No one knows what will be the future of a race so well protected by medical sciences. But we are confronted by much graver problems which demand immediate solution. While diarrhea, tuberculosis, diphtheria, typhoid fever, etc., are being eliminated, they are replaced by degenerative diseases. There are also a large number of actions of the nervous system and of the mind. In certain states the multitude of the insane confined in asylums exceeds that of the patients in all other hospitals. Like insanity, nervous disorders and intellectual weakness seem to become more frequent. They are the most active factors of individual misery and of the destruction of families. Mental deterioration is more dangerous for civilization than the infectious diseases to which hygienists and physicians have so far devoted their attention."[6]

Dr. Adler claims that all illness is a "dangerous corner" psychologically, but that illness may be made much less dangerous if the attitudes of courage and social-mindedness are developed. He maintains that "a child is psychologically affected by illness only in so far as he is not social minded."[7]

SOCIAL VALUE OF PLAY. For the child this social mindedness may be developed in play with other children. Group play, then, can be an invaluable aid in preventing neurotic tendencies from gaining headway during childhood illnesses. It

5. Adler, Alfred, *The Education of Children*, p. 192, New York, Greenberg (1930).
6. Carrel, Dr. Alexis, *Man the Unknown*, p. 20, New York, By the permission of the publishers, Harper and Brothers (1935).
7. Op. cit.

counteracts tendencies toward too great dependence upon adults; tends to prevent the fixation of habits of invalidism that purely medical and rest treatments tend to create and perpetuate; and its highly social character directs the child's attention away from himself to coöperation with other children in activities of an absorbing and joyous nature.

Play offsets the boredom and the dangers of psychic isolation so likely to develop in children confined to a hospital for a long period of time. Play also counteracts the tendency to self-pity created in part by over-sentimental parents and other relatives who shower the child with attentions. Play is particularly effective with isolated childrn. Play is the "language" of the child and the familiar world in which he acts freely and with confidence.

Throughout the hospital it was agreed that play banished homesickness and promoted in the children feelings of security and confidence in the hospital staff.

Even the simple change of casts disturbs some children. One extreme case was that of a boy of ten years. He was flushed, excited and nervous when brought to the operating unit. After playing some interesting games about twenty minutes, he seemed at ease and said, "I come for a change of casts and I play games all the time. I *like* it." He said that always before he had been sent directly to the operating room. He reported to the boys that he had had a good time in the hour of waiting. A conference with the head nurse revealed that he was a highly nervous child, and that invariably when the doctor came merely to examine his cast, he would have a vomiting spell.

Evidence from varied fields of research indicates that one of the greatest needs in our present civilization is emotional balance or stamina, the very foundation of our physical well-being and of our social, moral, and intellectual life. This is considered by many authorities more important than physical strength or intellectual brilliance. As Dr. Plant points out, "We live by what we feel rather than by what we know." Emotional imbalance is often revealed during illness and may even begin then, regardless of the duration of the illness. For the hospitalized child it is important that provision be made for nourishing and establishing his emotional development, since conditions of illness tend to exaggerate nervous tensions.

In summary, children engrossed in play have less time to feel sorry for themselves, less reason to build grudges against people and conditions, and are less likely to become habituated to invalidism. Even though children are subjected to long periods of hospital care, they need not be returned to their communities marked and scarred psychologically and emotionally, nor retarded mentally and rendered social misfits because of the neglect of stimulating interests and happy association with other children.

PLAY AS TREATMENT OF PROBLEM BEHAVIOR. The prevalence of problem behavior was one of the reasons for introducing the program of play. The hospital administrators, watchful of conditions, felt that something more than medical care was needed to improve conditions. For the very sick children, providing excellent medical and nursing care was sufficient, but for the children in the various stages of convalescence something additional was needed. It was difficult for the nurses to determine which were the normal unsatisfied needs of the children and which were merely their conscious or unconscious efforts to get attention as a relief from monotony. When given no interesting activities to counteract such conditions, the children had very little to think about except themselves and their illnesses. The great prevalence

of masturbation by the children was one evidence of the
need for providing activities interesting and absorbing to the
child.

The mere separation from their parents and the very
strangeness of the hospital situation were sufficient to give
many children a feeling of insecurity without any additional
suggestions. Sometimes such fears were taken on by the child
without the parent's saying a word, through the child's remarkable ability to sense the parent's feelings and unspoken
thought. Younger children seemed particularly sensitive to
psycho-motor tensions—the "language of muscle tensions."

Because hospital conditions are so foreign to children's
past experience, strange fancies and fears are likely to develop. The rooms are unlike any they have ever seen; the
immaculate cleanliness, the precision of the set-up, the pre-
dominance of white, the tense efficiency, all seem over-
emphasized to the child. Children seem to be particularly
susceptible to tension and hurry. Those brought into the
hospital for but a day have displayed homesickness, distrust,
and fear in varying degrees. Many children have been observed to have little time sense; even those ten or twelve
years of age have thought it was three o'clock in the afternoon when it was but nine-thirty or ten in the morning.
This intensified their fears that their parents had completely
forgotten them.

In the cases of many children false beliefs that doctors and
nurses will inflict pain upon them as a means of punishment are built up in them before they come to the hospital
for treatment. Too often for childish disobedience parents
actually threaten the child with what the doctor will do to
him. Also, many adults show a morbid interest in illness
and operations and seem to vie with one another in relating
gruesome details, in the presence of children.

Quite another type of problem behavior is likely to arise among healthy-minded children confined in the hospital. To those with fractures who were not really ill, to convalescents almost well enough to be dismissed, to diabetics in the milder stages of the disease, and to many orthopedic children, confinement in bed appeared highly irksome—an imprisonment to those full of vitality. In addition to the physical limitations, there was in the long-term cases a sense of being different from other children, a feeling of inadequacy very strong in some, particularly in the heart cases, the crippled, and the tubercular. Certain children withdrew into themselves; others showed exaggerated tendencies of aggressiveness and even anti-social behavior.

Confined to his bed for days, months, and sometimes years, the child not acutely ill has the impulse to leap and run and jump, to use his large muscles, all his body, all his senses for experimentation and learning. Wanting comrades, he is now held to routine, inactivity, quiet, even kept in isolation at times. Is it any wonder that problem behavior arises, that little faces grow wan and listless and tempers snap when nurses are compelled to keep them quiet?

In this hospital, responsibility for making children happy and for preventing the development of fears in them rested on the whole staff, as well as on the director of play, as a part of the daily care of the children. No morning or afternoon nursing care that did not provide for play in one of its many forms was considered complete. Nurses were encouraged to play with the children while giving routine physical care, to sing with them, to give them riddles and finger plays, folk and sense games, and to provide them with toys, books, or construction materials before leaving the room. In the earlier evening hours, they were expected to give them the quieter types of play. These play activities, experience has shown, not only helped to prevent and correct problem behavior on the part of the children but actually expedited routine nursing care because of the children's readiness to coöperate with the nurse who played with them even for a few minutes at a time.

In the wards where children were separated in cubicles by glass and steel partitions and where they were on precaution or in restraint, group feeling was promoted by play activities in which they all shared. Such play even though not executed in full detail seemed to make the children feel that they were doing the sort of thing well children do, whereas the usual precaution and strict isolation tended to build up the sense of being a social pariah or untouchable. The children responded heartily and enthusiastically to story telling, group singing and games, all of which created a feeling of gaiety that òvercame, in some degree, the physical barriers placed on or about them.

That nurses recognize the value of play in preventing destructive tendencies from gaining headway is evident by the following excerpts from their papers:

"Children are naturally restless and are even more so when confined to a hospital. They like to be the center of attention and can quite easily become behavior problems unless their attention can be diverted from themselves. Play is especially important in the care of cardiac and nephritic children. It's very hard for them to adhere to complete bed rest with limited body movements and they doubly appreciate any efforts made to help them pass the day. They usually become quite willing to stay in bed if given interesting diversions to help them forget their grievances. Play is practically a necessity in the convalescence of fracture and orthopedic patients. While confined, they are not usually ill. The time hangs heavily on their hands. They are apt to become peevish, irritable, and resentful that they must stay indoors and in bed."

"After all, play is of primary importance to the children. They eat well because they are emotionally satisfied. Behavior problems are at a minimum because they have a substitute to occupy their minds. Even the sick child is eager for play and perks up with interest. Many people think play is only for the well child, and the sick one is prevented from enjoying what his instinct craves. I notice in hospitals without play departments, youngsters will be restless far into the night when they should be asleep. With a day filled with adequate play the hospitalized child is pleasantly fatigued and ready for a night's rest. Better coöperation is secured from the child who is 'play satisfied.'"

How did these new attitudes originate? What factors developed the new ideas about children and their play? What awakened the realization that a child is not merely a miniature adult? Why has this been called "The Century of the Child"?

Since 1918 a number of events produced radical changes in education, the arts, psychology, mental hygiene, social work, industry, and the sciences. One important contribution came from the research that demonstrated the interdependence of the physical, mental, and emotional aspects of every human being. Many interesting books have been written in all these fields. Only a brief outline can be given here.

New attitudes toward children and their play came from war experiences that created new methods in education and treatment. Though play as part of treatment in illness can be traced through all history to primitive man, World War I spurred recognition of its unique values. Doctors performed miracles of healing in hospitals near the war fronts, but discovered the men were not ready to be returned to duty after the wounds healed. Some element was lacking. That led to experiments with music, games, and various types of recreation. The result was many more "miracles."

Thousands of veterans brought back to hospitals in the United States did not care to live or to see their wives, children, or parents. Doctors found progress blocked even with the best medical treatment. When recreational activities were experimented with, amazing changes happened. The Morale Officer at Camp Custer, Captain Bresnahan, reported:

"Sluggish wounds that failed to heal after months of treatment are now showing remarkable improvement wholly due to increased circulation through pleasurable exercises and to quickened interest in the normal things of life. Overseas boys are being brought back gradually to normal activities, thereby avoiding jars of too sudden transition to civil life."[8]

An expanded program of recreation became—and still is—a regular part of treatment in hospitals for the army, navy, and air forces. State institutions have followed, usually those treating mental patients, and now some city and private institutions.[9]

Children, as a nation's chief resource for the future, became a special concern. In World War I, doctors treating servicemen were concerned with the prevalence of personality problems traced to early childhood experiences. Nursery schools, established as a war measure, increased understanding of early childhood. Colleges and health agencies intensified research. New methods of treatment for the crippled, blind, mentally retarded, and emotionally disturbed were

8. Boyd, Neva L., *Hospital and Bedside Games,* Chicago, FitzSimons, (1945), p. 4.

9. Consulting Service, *Toward Life and Health, A Special Report,* New York, National Recreation Association, n.d.

patterned after those used in hospitals for soldiers, which were said to have advanced medical science by ten years.

Furthermore, many thousands of men and women experienced, in the various Special Services for adequate recreational opportunities for enlisted personnel, the values of recreational activities new to them, which our government provided on a world-wide scale in both wars.[10] All these experiences stimulated new evaluations of play in many fields. A more general understanding and respect for children and their play made more people aware that childhood experiences were important in determining attitudes and actions. Play was recognized as nature's way for the child to grow, to learn about himself and his relations to others. Social conditioning was traced to early infancy with good mothering the cause for better development by petting, singing, playing etc.

More than half the infants in hospitals died from debility in the early half of this century. Studies showed that those with this "wasting disease" came from the best hospitals and homes, while those from the poorest homes but with good mothers overcame physical handicaps of this first year of their lives, and flourished. Explanations of these physical, mental, and social gains are given in *Rights of Infants,* the result of eight years of research by Dr. Margaret Ribble in Boston, New York, and Vienna. She claims tiny babes sense the mother's feelings of love or of lack of love no matter how she may seek to mask her feelings of dislike for the infant's care, and that the foundations for either cooperative or unsocial attitudes are laid by the mother.[11]

10. Romney, G. Ott, *Off the Job Living,* Chapter VII, New York, Barnes (1945).

11. Ribble, Dr. Margaret, *Rights of Infants,* New York, Columbia University Press (1945).

Modern hospitals are changing their rules. Some in the maternity wards, where formerly newborn babes were taken immediately to wards of their own, are welcoming frequent visits as well as overnight stays in the child's room during the acute stage of illness as an aid in hastening cure. Patients are dismissed as early as possible since home is considered the best place, especially for infants. Where foster care is imperative, the newer methods attempt to keep the links between the relatives and the child by frequent visits, by day care or short group and foster home treatment, and frequent check-ups on the child's development.[12]

William Goldfarb's tests of children institutionalized early in life, as compared with those brought up in good foster homes, showed them more demanding of attention, more retarded mentally and socially, more aggressive, apathetic, and aimless. He thinks the sense of not being wanted, of not "belonging" caused by the routines and impersonal conditions in large institutions, build the idea that "adults always let you down," which leads to delinquency.[13]

Whether or not one accepts the idea that attitudes are firmly fixed in infancy and not changed by later experiences, there is much evidence that more human relations and continued study of each period of development are needed. The increasing numbers needing treatment for neurotic disorders and mental disabilities show that need.

The Midcentury White House Conference on Children and Youth emphasized the new attitude. It stressed the need for more study of human values, more care for the emotional

---

12. Witmer, Helen L. and Ruth Kotinsky, *Personality in the Making*, Fact Finding Report, Midcentury White House Conference, Chapter IV, New York, Harper and Brothers (1952).

13. Goldfarb, William, "The Effects of Early Institutional Care on Adolescent Personality," *Journal of Experimental Education*, Vol. 12 (1943), pp. 106-129.

and spiritual factors, and pointed to many possible advances in methods and understanding. Instead of piecemeal treatment by specialists, each child should be considered as a "whole person." Education of physicians, nurses, parents and teachers in more human relationships were *advocated, particularly for the convalescent children,* so that the social and spiritual needs could be met as well as the physical and mental.[14]

Recent experiments in the control of life processes and of disease indicate in the near future a possible life expectancy of more than a hundred years. Today, many aged persons brought up in the Puritan tradition of work and of leisure have few interests outside their work. After compulsory retirement many lose interest in living, and crowd rest homes and hospitals. The childhood years offer the best opportunity for learning the greatest number of activities that can serve as a foundation for development in adult years. Nash's twenty-year study of a thousand college graduates showed sixty per cent of their recreation interests began before the age of ten, and seventy per cent before twelve. Young children engaged in forty different kinds of activities, which diminished by half in adolescence.[15]

A second industrial revolution because of automation is on its way, providing more leisure and a shorter work week and increasing the importance of preparation for that free time. The first such revolution reduced factory workers to mere tools of the machine, with women and children as well as the men working exceedingly long hours. This second revolution offers the opportunity for the finest develop-

14. Witmer, Helen L. and Ruth Kotinsky, *Personality in the Making, op. cit.,* Chapter XIV.. and *Proceedings of the Midcentury White House Conference on Children and Youth,* "Summaries of Work Group Opinions," Part V, Raleigh, N. C., Health Publications (1951).

15. Nash, J. B., *Philosophy of Recreations and Leisure,* St. Louis, Mosby (1953).

ment of all persons. A. R. Martin, M.D., says recreation is
the only field concentrating on preparation for leisure and
points out in his article, "Recreation as a Positive Force in
Preventive Medicine," how it can re-establish the natural
biological rhythm in the promotion of health.[16]

In modern times both management and labor have found
recreational activities so valuable for workers and their
families that the location of a new plant is determined by a
survey of recreation facilities and "industry now expends
eight hundred million dollars each year—in and out of its
plants," says Rudolph F. Bannow, president of the National
Association of Manufacturers, because "nothing is more important to the physical and emotional health of the men
and women in industry than proper recreation activities."[17]
George Meany, president of AFL-CIO, states: "The solu-
tions to many of our most crucial social problems are cur-
rently being sought in that area."[18] What a contrast to
colonial times when the fashionable new game of baseball
was a privilege of the leisure class! The umpire wore a high
silk hat and carried an umbrella to protect himself from
the sun. If laborers wanted to play, they could only do so in
the very early morning hours before work began.[19]

But with all the material advances in industry and science,
many find that possession of material things in themselves
fails to give lasting satisfaction. With the hydrogen bomb,

16. Martin, A. R., *"Recreation as a Positive Force in Preventive Medicine,"*
    "Recreation, p. 265 (September 1959), New York, National Recreation
    Association.

17. Bannow, Rudolph and George Meany, "What is Expected of Recreation
    in the Next Ten Years." *Recreation,* p. 14, (January 1960). New York
    National Recreation Association.

18. *Ibid.*

19. Dulles, Foster Rhea, *America Learns to Play.* New York, Appleton-
    Century-Crofts (1940).

possible flight to the planets, and new realization of the interdependence of all persons and nations, new evaluations arise as attention is focused on human needs beyond the material.

Demand for more and better leadership in the recreation field led to a great increase in colleges and universities offering training. Records show five such schools in 1940, thirty-five in 1942, and sixty-five with undergraduate and graduate degrees by January 1960. These do not supply enough leaders to meet present needs.[20]

A new profession is developing to meet hospital needs, with a Council for the Advancement of Hospital Recreation, created by the American Recreation and the National Recreation associations, setting standards in 1956 for registration of recreational personnel for the ill and handicapped. In 1953 the National Recreation Association established the Consulting Service on Recreation for the Ill and the Handicapped with Beatrice H. Hill as director. The NRA Recreation Book Center started in 1953 has over 800 titles on every phase of play and recreation. For more recent summaries of present-day thinking and planning see: "What's New in Recreation for the Ill and Handicapped," by Beatrice Hill; "Learning to Live with Leisure Time" by Paul Douglas; "Recreation's Role in Hospitals" by Dorothy Taafe; and "Recreation's Challenge" by Harold Meyer in the *American Recreation Annual*, Vol. 1, New York, American Recreation Society (1960).

20. Sutherland, W. C., "Curriculum Strategy," *Recreation*, p. 20 (January 1960). New York, National Recreation Association.

CHAPTER 2

THE VALUE OF TRADITIONAL PLAY ACTIVITIES

Just as all education has always utilized the outstanding contributions of the past so the forms of play and art of the past are utilized in the development of the child. The supposition that the child has within himself sufficient resources to create play comparable to these treasures of the past without recourse to his cultural heritage is false.

Our culture in the United States, evolving as it does from many racial streams, tends to enlarge the child's viewpoint and develop his sympathy for many peoples. Folklore from these racial sources abounds in play activities such as games, stories, songs, and other arts that are peculiarly effective in promoting sympathetic understanding.

To be sure, the mere acquisition of the past contributions is not sufficient education in itself, nor is it our purpose merely to fit the child into existing culture but rather that the past shall serve to stimulate and inspire his own creative abilities.

In this era of searching study of democratic procedures amid chaotic indications of a changing world, group play methods in traditional play activities deserve careful study. Their values in giving children first-hand experience in carrying out democratic principles on the level of their understanding in each stage of their development, need emphasizing in planning the education of children in a democracy.

GROUP GAMES. As a part of this cultural heritage, traditional games deserve special emphasis because of children's enthusiastic response to them. The very content of these games takes the player's imagination far away from the commonplace in both time and space, and because they are the product of generations of spontaneous play-behavior they tend to produce similar play-behavior in the children. Furthermore, they serve as efficacious means of coöperative interaction. Not only are they on the child's level of understanding but in playing them thought and action correspond and call forth integrated behavior.

Hundreds of these games are almost wholly non-competitive and many of them, accompanied by songs, call for simultaneous action of the whole playing group. Such situations sweep even the most apathetic children into happy coöperation and enable them to share the stimulation of the total unit. Thus it is that the coöperative type of group game carries the child forward in development to a far greater degree than he could possibly go alone. In such games he gains acquaintance with persons of different temperament and learns to make his own adjustments with them. He gains experience in coöperatively creating happiness for all concerned within the framework of the game. Thus he is at once freely creative and rigorously law abiding. The child is not following the dictates of a leader. He does not "sacrifice his wishes to those of the group" but rather he and his fellows jointly coöperate in creating their own satisfactions and abstracting their own values.

Group play properly selected presents a challenge that the child can and almost invariably does accept. In his spontaneous efforts to meet the demands of the play situation, strain and conflict are dissolved and potentialities released. When play is wholehearted, its rules and all other requirements are voluntarily carried on with exactness by the players. Its discipline, instead of cramping initiative, organizes and releases new energies and reveals alluring adventure as the players get deeper into the subtleties of play. This leads the individual to grow, no matter what his age may be at the starting point.

Concerning play, Miss Boyd out of her wide experience writes:

"Thus, when games used as educational nutriment, are well correlated with the growth and development of the players, they induce normal patterns of behavior characteristic of no other activity. Moreover, the players abstract, or learn each according to his own growth, development, and sensitivity.[1]

Two examples will serve to illustrate:

May is a Canadian Indian who was sent to a hospital for treatment when she was twelve years old to have both crippled legs straightened. Cruel treatment at home, where she was found crawling along the floor like an animal, had so frightened her she could not or would not talk. According to all the tests applied she was graded as feebleminded. The doctors, nurses, and social workers tried every language and method they knew, but there was no response from May in words. Her eyes fluttered queerly at every approach. She had been in the hospital ten months when a teacher and a play specialist were added to the staff. They found May in a ward with seven others who ranged in ages from two to six years. May, now nearly thirteen years old, could

[1]. Boyd, Neva L., "Play as a Means of Social Adjustment," *Journal of Health and Physical Education*, Vol. VII, p. 410 (September, 1936).

say a word or two and was just learning to walk with crutches for very short periods under the careful direction of the physiotherapist. She shuffled along, very, very slowly, dragging one foot flatly after the other, her whole attention concentrated on herself in her efforts to walk.

The children, including May, spent most of their time in bed, nevertheless many forms of group play such as singing, games, rhythm play, stories, simple dramatizations of their own devising or of folk games and stories, were possible with the whole group participating. May took part in all these activities, grinning with seemingly equal favor on all types even though they were the simpler kinds which are usually the choice of children under six years of age.

At first, when the children were given their individual choices in play materials, May merely pointed to what she wanted but within three weeks of group play she said slowly, distinctly, but in stilted fashion, "I want-that-game-over-there." She played, happily, increasingly more difficult games, appeared to concentrate on the games and to forget herself while playing. Her guarded diffidence was less apparent and she welcomed the play leaders with beaming smiles. The play director began to wonder if the child were as subnormal as she was believed to be, and tested May's responses in several types of traditional play activities suitable to nine- or ten-year-old children. May did so well in these the play director beckoned her to play Chinese Checkers with a bright fifteen-year-old crippled girl in the next room, and seemingly paid no special attention to May manipulating her crutches en route. Eager to play, the child came along steadily so absorbed in getting into the next room so that she could play the game she made very good time and handled her crutches and brace-bound legs rather easily, her attention concentrated on her destination rather than on herself. She carried her part very nicely in the games that followed with the older girls in this ward, and repeatedly walked in easily with her crutches whenever games were to be played, but reverted to her slow shuffle whenever she had to practice walking as a physical exercise.

May now talked with increasing fluency and was even observed to walk from bed to bed without her crutches when completely absorbed in a game. Her school work improved. She showed more confidence in herself and in other people. Her eyes fluttered less. During an epidemic, May was transferred to another ward where no group activities were permitted. Her behavior reverted to what it had been in her earlier days in the hospital and changed for the better only when she was sent back to the ward where group activities again absorbed her and made her forget herself. Group play demonstrated that May was not feebleminded, gave her the incentive to behave like an intelligent, social being, with the result that she could now receive further education in an Indian School where admission had formerly been denied her because she was thought to be feebleminded.

The results obtained with traditional activities used as group play, both in May's case and in the one that follows, were apparent in a period of less than three months.

Walter is a deaf boy who cannot talk. The teachers at The School for the Deaf, where he is a resident pupil, considered him very poor in school work and a "discipline problem" very disturbing to the others in his class as well as to the teachers. They were glad to give him "funny papers" during school hours as the best means of keeping him quiet even for a short time.

A diabetic condition made hospital treatment necessary. Two weeks after his admission to the hospital the boys in his ward reported that he still would take no part in any of their activities, and the new school teacher there found him unresponsive, a negative personality rather than a disturbing problem since he was confined to his bed in accordance with hospital practice. The play director decided to experiment with various traditional games. Three of the boys in this ward could be up and around so she asked them if they cared for a game of Bird Stealers. (This is a game, with colored bird cards that come in boxes of baking soda, played according to the rules of the old game of Casino.) They had never heard of the game but thought they would like to try it and gathered around the bedside table which the play director drew up close to Walter's bed. Walter, too, was asked if he wanted to play but he shook his head. He watched indifferently as the cards were dealt and refused a hand when the boys sought to include him. As the game progressed he was observed to watch the play intently, so on the second deal the play director offered him a hand of cards which he accepted. He played with the boys an hour and a half, expressing his approval by smiles and grunts, until the noon meal interrupted all play activities in the ward.

After noon rest hour Walter wanted to play the game again and tried to get it by grunting, pointing, and finally by writing notes to the nurses asking for cards. A nurse reported this to the play director remarking in puzzled and rather shocked tones, "And you know we have no *cards* in *this* hospital." Walter smiled with delight when the bird cards were brought to him and he played again with the three boys until the supper hour. From that time Walter became an accepted member of the group, sharing in whatever group activities interested the other boys in the ward. In team games of bean bag target he learned to do single and double additions, and Hang-a-Man proved a delightful way to do spelling. Learning became fun for him and thereafter he accepted school lessons cheerfully. The hospital staff considered Walter a bright, sociable boy easy to get along with. Returned to The School for the Deaf after two and a half months of treatment, his teachers there reported how he taught the games he had learned at the hospital to the boys in his school, and remarked with pleasure on his changed attitudes and behavior.

Furthermore, he seems to have made the hospital experience an easier one for the other boys and girls from his school who were sent to the hospital afterwards for tonsil or adenoid operations. Tears that flowed freely and fears that arose in this strange place where no one knew how to convey ideas in the language of the deaf were brushed aside with beaming smiles when the play leaders started the games which Walter had told them they might expect in the hospital.

IMPRESSIONS OF PLAY EXPERIENCES ON CHILDREN. Many adults are quite unconcerned about the quality of a child's play and feel almost any activity will do that keeps him occupied. They fail to see how thoroughly impressions register in the total personality of the child during his play, how even seemingly very insignificant details are recalled months, and even years later. There are many examples of the impression that group activities made on children in a hospital situation. Three boys asked for a story to be continued that had been interrupted seven weeks previously. For the benefit of the newcomers in the ward the boys sketched the first part of the story. They remembered details, subtle events of the plot, and descriptions, remarkably well.

Said a newly admitted boy of eleven, after playing several

games, "Say, are you the one that played with us when we were having our tonsils out?" He was asked, "When did you have them out?" "Oh, about eight months ago, and we played that game where you blind your eyes and feel things."

A physician and his wife reported the vivid memory of their four-year-old son, who two years previously had been frightened when admitted for a tonsil operation and play had been used to quiet him. He recalled the colors, shapes, and details of the Fish Pond game used to stop his crying before the operation.

Another boy was much pleased that every child was given fresh valentines to send to his friends. "Say, this hospital thinks of everything, doesn't it? Are you, by any chance, the lady that played games with us before tonsil operations? Gee, didn't we have fun! You remember me, don't you?" To test his memory he was asked what games were played, whereupon he named several. In consulting the records later, his list was found to be accurate.

A volunteer play leader promised five-year-old Flozelle that next time she came to the ward she would bring her some little dishes to play with. The volunteer obtained work in a distant city, and when she returned to the hospital for a visit more than a year later, Flozelle's first words of greeting to her were, "Did you bring those dishes to play with?"

In larger wards, moving the beds near enough to make certain group activities possible brought joy and a feeling of unity in the group. "Don't you remember how you pulled our beds together and we played stories?" was the first statement of a crippled girl after an absence of several months.

Another quite common attitude of adults is that prizes and rewards are necessary for successful play, to stimulate interest in activities or to give a party flavor to some celebration. Very often the need for artificial stimulation arises because such anemic, made-up types of play are selected. But with traditional games, songs, stories and other play activities that survive the centuries, the dross has been washed away. These activities afford the children satisfactions without resort to artificial aids.

REWARDS AND PRIZES. Since prizes and rewards, which so largely defeat play, have such a foothold in our schools and playgrounds that they are likely to be carried into our hospitals for children, a warning against them seems justifiable. Prizes and material rewards are directly contrary to genuine play. The essence of play is spontaneity, psychological absorption, and free expression. In playing groups freedom, spontaneity, and psychological intimacy grow out of cooperative social interaction. Play is an emotional attitude—the spirit in which the individual does something because he wants to do it for "the fun of it." Although when truly playing, he feels free to express his ideas and emotions, he is nevertheless subjected to the discipline inherent in whatever he is undertaking, be it a game, a song, or even what might by another be considered work.

Prizes and rewards are alien to play and tend to nullify it. Children readily sense the disharmony and even the sharp conflict they tend to create. Children need no artificial inducements to play; the activities are fun and give sufficient satisfaction in themselves. When a child plays, he is absorbed in the activity, even wholly unconfused by rapid changes of character, and new phases of activity that develop in the process of the game. But when prizes or rewards are introduced, his wholehearted attention in the activity is diverted to a consciousness of his efforts to win. He is forced to watch himself in relation to the activity and to the other children, and this restricted, antagonistic, and artificially imposed effort produces the counterfeit of real play.

Rewarding the excellent gives cause for rejoicing only to the winner. In play, the unity of functioning harmoniously within the individual and in his relation to the other players is split into antagonistic forces by rewards and prizes. It is highly probable that this overemphasis on competition confuses, distracts, and disturbs any child, and particularly a sick one. He may show his confusion in different ways— withdrawing "into his shell," becoming irritable or discontented, or glorying in the opportunity provided by adults for domineering, for acting aggressively, and for determining to win at all costs. Again, he may suffer from varying degrees of overstimulation. The adult who persists in using rewards with children can always comfort himself with the old alibi that "You can't change human nature," and is likely to blame the children's objectionable conduct on anything except the prizes he has offered them.

Regarding competition, Kirkpatrick points out the falsity of using the struggle for existence theory as a basis for belief in the necessity of competition. He maintains that the studies of physicists and biologists prove that conflict was exceptional. "Cooperation rather than conflict is the dominant characteristic of all intelligent human behavior." [2]

The fact that rewards and prizes destroy the essence of play and are detrimental to happiness when used with children in a hospital is a sufficient reason for their rejection. Authorities in other fields who have written recently in condemnation of rewards, prizes, and overemphasis on com-

2. Kirkpatrick, Edwin A., *Mental Hygiene for Effective Living*, p. 178, Appleton-Century (1934).

petition are Anderson,[3] Boyd,[4] Plant,[5] Glover and Dewey,[6] and Davis.[7]

As the child participates increasingly in non-competitive group activities, free from distracting rewards, he realizes through actual experience something of the meaning of such terms as freedom, loyalty, coöperation, and similar abstractions which might otherwise be meaningless to him. Thus children are helped to see themselves in relation to others and to realize that their desires are somehow related to those of others.

Dr. van de Wall says, "It is the mission of social education to surround the inmate (in the hospital) with an environment abounding in emotions, ideas, plans, techniques, activities and personalities that make living for social goals the preferred way of individual wish fulfillment."[8]

When the inmates are children, such an environment necessitates supplying play of a fine quality, stimulating play that frees a child's abilities through his wholehearted acceptance of its satisfactions, its disciplines. The goal which Dr. van de Wall outlines will be more nearly reached when children are given free access to those play activities which have stood the test of generations of use. Rich cultural resources from many racial streams are at our disposal, vast supplies of games, stories, songs, and other arts practically untouched in current hospital practice. When the values in

3. Anderson, Harold H., *Children in the Family*, pp. 178-81, New York, Appleton-Century (1937).
4. Boyd, Neva L., "Play as a Means of Social Adjustment," *Journal of Health and Physical Education*, Vol. VII, p. 412 (September, 1936).
5. Plant, James S., *Personality and the Cultural Pattern*, pp. 295-6 and Chapters XI and XII. New York, The Commonwealth Fund (1937).
6. Glover, K. and Evelyn Dewey, *Children of the New Day*, pp. 233-235, New York, Appleton-Century (1934).
7. Davis, John Eisele, *Play and Mental Health*, New York, Barnes (1938).
8. van de Wall, Willem, *Music in Institutions*, p. 46, New York, Russell Sage Foundation (1936).

play are better understood and when it is realized that their constructive use, particularly with children who are handicapped in any way, requires professional education in play, hospital administrators will no longer be satisfied with merely supplying children with toys or other play equipment, and providing an inadequate program of play.

Scientific research in the past fifty years in biology, psychology, and social studies contradicts nineteenth-century ideas that competition is the law of life, and that it is "natural" for the fittest to survive. They state that those in power in the early days of the Industrial Revolution in Europe used Malthus and the earlier statements of Darwin as an excuse to justify their exploitation of young children, men, and women in factories and mines, and their own right to leisure. Also, pioneer conditions in our own country encouraged ideas of "each man for himself" and "leisure the devil's handiwork" for all but landlords. Researchers claim that highly competitive practices are outmoded, obsolete, and contradictory to present-day needs. They point out the effects of such practices psychologically, socially, and ethically and warn that this modern era demands mutual aid if we are to survive.

Ashley Montagu, anthropologist at Rutgers University and consultant to UNESCO, reviews the recent findings in various scientific fields in his book *On Being Human,* which prove cooperation is a basic drive in insects, animals, and human beings. Other writers, also, show the need of re-evaluating practices of our highly competitive society in terms of modern needs:

Arnold, Arnold, *How to Play with Your Child,* Chapter III, New York, Ballantyne (1955).

Adler, Alfred, *Social Interest: A Challenge to Mankind,* New York, Putnam's (1938).

Dixon, C. Madeleine, *Keep Them Human,* New York, Day (1941).
Fromm, Erich, *Escape from Freedom,* New York, Rinehart (1941).
_____, *Sane Society,* New York, Rinehart (1955).
May, Rollo, *Man's Search for Himself,* New York, Norton (1953).
Mumford, Lewis, *The Conduct of Life,* Chapter IX, New York, Harcourt, Brace (1951).
Nouy, Lecompte du, *Human Destiny,* New York, Longman's, Green (1947).
Riesman, David, *Individualism Reconsidered,* Chicago, Free Press (1954).
_____, *The Lonely Road,* New York, Doubleday Anchor (1953).
Russell, Bertrand, *Education and the Good Life,* New York, Simon and Schuster (1951).
_____, *New Hopes for a Changing World,* New York, Simon and Schuster (1951).

CHAPTER 3

ORGANIZATION AND ADMINISTRATION
OF THE DEPARTMENT OF PLAY

THE NEED OF A PROFESSIONAL DIRECTOR. The usual picture that comes to mind with the mention of play in a children's hospital is that of a volunteer seated at the bedside of a child reading a story, handing out toys and gifts to the sick or, perhaps more often, that of a small troupe of entertainers putting on a musical or dramatic performance for the children. In short, the idea seems to be that play is something gratuitously added merely to keep the child quiet and amused, after the physical care has been attended to, something almost anyone can do—a matter of kindly intentions rather than of educational insight and skill.

Many adults think they have provided for the play needs of convalescent children when they have given them playthings, such as finished toys or busy-work for the purpose of keeping them occupied and out of mischief. Likewise these adults take for granted that if toys and play materials are given to children they will be resourceful and use them intelligently. If the child does not know how to use this equipment, he is often considered stupid, destructive or peevish. But how few children, beyond babyhood, are satisfied with playthings alone. Playthings do not constitute play, at best they are but instruments with a limited function in a wide field of play.

Too much emphasis placed upon material equipment of

any kind tends to restrict the free exercise of the child's imagination and to prevent resourcefulness and inventiveness. When nurses or teachers are required to provide materials to keep the convalescent child busy and amused, all too often they give him something to copy, some outline to be filled in with crayolas, or traced figures to be cut out with scissors. What is needed is not so much the material equipment, as the incentive, the imaginative drive to function creatively. Given that, all materials, no matter how commonplace, become the instruments for zestful expression.

For the hospitalized children, play must be chosen with due regard to the particular disease and supervised intelligently, lest more harm than good result. Their play should be under the direction of one who in addition to being able to observe and interpret the behavior of children in each play situation, is also able to estimate with some degree of accuracy the effects of different diseases upon the child's temperament and personality and to select his play activities accordingly.

To the play leader lacking such ability a rosy cheeked, mentally alert patient may appear quite capable of playing an exciting game, whereas the very color of his cheeks and the hyperactivity he manifests may be due to an illness in which the more quieting types of activities are needed. A well-intentioned person with a knowledge of games and accustomed to active, healthy children and to the competitive methods in general use in schools and playgrounds may do great harm by choosing games for convalescent children without regard to their condition. Such lack of knowledge of the patient's illness may result in other types of harm, also; for example, the uncoördinated movements and impaired speech which characterize spastic paralysis may lead one to believe that a child is dull and stupid when he is in fact highly intelligent. Or his condition may induce pity when what he needs is encouragement, success in his efforts, an environment of serenity, and freedom from every possible strain.

As a safeguard for hospitalized children, it is imperative for all persons entrusted with their play to consult with the head nurse in charge of them, regarding those on the ward who need special care.

Although play activities should be selected with regard to the types of disease, the tendency to center attention too exclusively either on the disease or on the play activity should be avoided. It is the child that should be the center of attention, and his needs should be the starting point in selecting play activities for him. But confining attention to his immediate needs alone would tend to prevent a more complete consideration of the whole child and of the remote as well as the immediate effects of the activity upon him.

The observation of many sick children reveals that their recovery is often startlingly rapid. Frequently they are mentally and emotionally alert and vigorous while still handicapped physically. Again apathy and irritability may be merely the expression of boredom due to enforced rest and restricted movement rather than the result of the illness. When this is the case, this bordom may often be made to disappear as if by magic with the introduction of stimulating activities within their abilities to perform.

THE TECHNIQUE OF PLAY LEADERSHIP. When the play leader selects activities that are coördinated with the development of the children and succeeds in presenting the game, song, story, or other form of play so that it affords the children enjoyment the first time it is presented, there is little need to fear for their reception of it later. Children almost invariably look forward to repeating over and over an activity that they have enjoyed when first introduced.

The play leader must know not only what games to play, how to present them to the children, and how to play them, but how long to play so that interest does not lag or the patients become overstimulated or fatigued.

In introducing the game, the main outline should be presented by the leader, details being worked out gradually as the game progresses. Introductory remarks should be few, simple and clear, because long explanations merely confuse children. Also, the leader must be watchful continually of the social, as well as the physical effects of play, for it is important for the children to enjoy playing with each other. She must know when to play along with the children, when to be all there "in spirit" though never saying a word, and how far actual leadership should be given to insure independent action and growth on the part of the children themselves.

The plan of having a director of play on the hospital staff not only gives coherence and greater unity in carrying out a program of activities; it gives, also, coherence and greater unity in the treatment and development of the children. In observing children playing in groups, the play leader has unequaled opportunities for discovering many aspects of children's behavior and personality that are not revealed in such contacts as that of the doctor, the nurse, the social worker, or the psychiatrist, all of whom use case work, or individual methods of approach and treatment. Playing with children in groups, the physical, mental, emotional, social, and moral aspects of behavior are spontaneously and unreservedly expressed and may be treated as a related whole, not only at the time the activity is in progress, but as a continuous process. This synthesis tends to provide a comprehensive and accurate picture of problem behavior, thereby facilitating analysis and treatment.

Faulty conceptions of play and its uses have too often resulted in inadequate provision for the many-sided needs of children in institutions. For a more complete release of the potential abilities in a child one must have an understanding of more than one age-period. The education of professional play directors covers the development of all ages including infancy, childhood, adolescence, and adulthood, and not to just one stage of a child's growth such as the pre-school or kindergarten period. Intensive training limited to one age-range, fine though it is for its special purpose, is inadequate to the hospital situation and gives but partial training in viewing the child in his complete development. The wide diversity of interests in children from seven to about ten or eleven years is particularly noteworthy, as well as the special needs of youth.

An adequate play program for the children of a wide diversity of ages is the responsibility of the director of play. With this comes the correlation of the entertainment and educational activities provided for the children not only by persons within the hospital but by outside agencies and volunteer workers. From the administrative standpoint this includes the instruction of the nurses, the volunteer play leaders, and the patients' parents in play activities that will aid the child's development while he is in the hospital.

If the values of play as entertainment, as a therapeutic aid, as mental hygiene, as a means of understanding child behavior and of aiding his total development are to be used, a thorough professional education is needed.

METHODS OF ORGANIZATION USED AT THE CHILDREN'S MEMORIAL HOSPITAL. In an attempt to give its patients experiences compatible with childhood, the administrators undertook the promotion of a full-time program of play as an integral part of its care of children.

Prior to 1930 the hospital had no organized play, although volunteer workers occasionally read to individual children, entertained them with programs of various types, and contributed both gifts and entertainment for holiday occasions. In the fall of 1930 a staff nurse from this hospital registered for a course in The Social Aspects of Play in the Sociology Department of Northwestern University. Early in the course she foresaw the applicability of play to a children's hospital. Her discussion of this possibility with the instructor resulted finally in the launching of an experimental program of play on the larger wards, the work being done by six advanced university students as required field work. In addition, during the year, twenty lectures and demonstrations were given the nurses and other staff members on the subject of play by the instructor of the university course. The following summer a part-time leader was added to the staff. This led to the engaging of a full-time director of play, who continued as a member of the staff from 1932 to 1938.

The hospital has a capacity of two hundred and fifty-two beds and served approximately four thousand children each year, of which about ninety-seven per cent were either charity patients or those whose parents were able to pay but part of the cost of their hospital care. Practically all patients were confined to their beds, many of them for long periods of time. Play was given to all children with the exception of infants and those very ill, the age limit being thirteen years, and was considered an important part of the care of children throughout the day.

The director of play began her work at eight o'clock in the morning, conducting play with the children scheduled for operations. Nurses played with the other children while giving routine care. Special wards were open to play leaders from nine-thirty in the morning until the luncheon hour. At two-thirty or three in the afternoon, after rest hour, play began again and this period proved to be the most convenient for the volunteer play leaders. In the earlier evening hours after the children's four-thirty supper, quiet types of play were given by the nurses.

With six wards averaging from thirty to thirty-five children each, there was little danger of overstimulation through giving too much play. The number of children and the limited number of nurses and play leaders, together with the routine medical care, including rest periods, sleep, and meals, set limits to the children's play and left them dependent upon their own resources much of the time.

EXPERIMENTATION AS A BASIS OF PROGRAM DEVELOPMENT. In introducing play into the hospital, the attitude of the director was experimental; no set program of activities was imposed, but whenever there appeared actual situations in which the children might be helped by play, various types of play activities were experimented with for the purpose of discovering their beneficial possibilities. Although, as they became familiar with the various types of play, the children were encouraged to make their own choices, the play leaders were expected to exercise initiative in leadership and in introducing new activities. These experimental policies determined the way in which the scope of the work was to develop and resulted in adding from five to eight new types of activities each year, such as play before operations, display of play materials for the guidance of parents, play programs for dispensary patients and visitors.

The work of the director of the department included the

teaching of courses for student nurses and volunteer play leaders; the conducting of demonstrations of play in the hospital; the giving of lectures and the discussing of play for groups outside the hospital such as nurses, hospital administrators, and women's clubs. Also, the director of play gave personal supervision to all volunteer workers in the department, and general supervision of the children's librarian.

For a period of approximately six years, the director experimented with play as a means of providing for the emotional, mental, and social needs of the children, and for making them feel more contented and secure while in the hospital. Play was considered neither a distraction nor a mere entertainment, by the hospital staff, but an educational experience necessary for every child's development.

VOLUNTEER WORKERS. Two hundred and thirty-two volunteer workers, or approximately forty per year, gave assistance in the Department of Play between March, 1932, and December, 1937. They were of two types—those who had had some training in activities such as games, songs, stories, nature study, and handcrafts, and those untrained in work with children. The majority of those in the first group were upper-class students in the Group Work and Recreation Field of Concentration in the Sociology Department of Northwestern University, who came to the hospital to conduct play on the wards, as a part of their field work. The untrained volunteer workers came from many sources, and two types of work were available to them: office work for the department of play and play with the children. While there were always records and cards to be typed, hundreds of scenic cards to be organized for lantern slides, and library books and play equipment to be mended and organized, most volunteer workers preferred to play with the children.

During the spring of 1932, seventeen volunteers helped with play. As has been said elsewhere, the Beginner's Course in play for nurses was also open to volunteer workers, and, in fact, all volunteer workers without experience in the education of children were required to attend at least four sessions before going on the wards to play with the children. In October, 1932, the first five volunteers attended this class in play. In November thirteen enrolled, nine of whom voluntarily completed the course of eight lessons. Later, some of these volunteer workers attended eight additional class sessions. Within a year, twenty-three volunteer workers had had varying amounts of class instruction.

Volunteer workers claimed that the practical demonstrations and participation in activities that constituted the class work gave them better understanding of children and of the hospital and more satisfaction in their volunteer work than they would otherwise have had. From the administrative standpoint, it raised the standards of play conducted by the volunteer workers and changed their contribution from the customary reading to the children or merely entertaining them, to giving them the opportunity of active participation in the more vital educational process which characterized the play program. In spite of compulsory class attendance and the requirement of higher standards of work, the volunteer workers practically doubled in one year. This policy of requiring a minimum attendance of classes in play before beginning work in the wards was permanently adopted.

These volunteer workers gave valuable service. They encountered difficulties because of their lack of understanding of hospital routine and rules, which of necessity are strict when sick and convalescent children are being dealt with. For the purpose of safeguarding the children and of insuring satisfaction for the volunteer worker, a printed booklet briefly setting forth the reasons for the hospital rules and offering suggestions regarding activities, dress, and the like was formulated by a committee. For more specific understanding, as far as play was concerned, the director of play held informal conferences with the volunteers before and after their work on the wards. These workers were required to keep brief but accurate records of the activities in which they engaged each time, together with the ward, the number of children played with, and the time spent.

Among the many outstanding contributions of the volunteer workers was that made by three young women who played soft-toned musical instruments—the zither-harp, accordion, guitar, and flute—accompanying and leading the children's singing rather than providing them with the more usual entertainment. Other skilled workers taught sewing and needlepoint to the older girls; and still others, variously equipped, helped with games, dramatic play, story telling, puppet shows, parties, and special celebrations.

RULES FOR HOSPITAL VOLUNTEERS

1. BE REGULAR.
2. Appointments for interviews or visiting in the hospital are necessary in order to insure satisfaction to the volunteers and to avoid interruption of important hospital routine. Promptness for all appointments is also desirable.
3. Volunteers who wish to work directly with the children are urged to take advantage of the classes in play for children in a hospital, which are given regularly from 1—2 p.m. on Thursdays.
4. The recreational director can be reached only during her office hours, 11:30—12 a.m., and 2:00—2:30 p.m.
5. Volunteers and visitors entering wards must wear smocks or hospital gowns. Rubber-heeled shoes are desirable.

6. Lockers for your smocks are provided in the Recreation Office. If you own your smock, mark it with your name inside the collar.

7. A record of volunteer work is kept. Please fill in and sign your card.

8. Instructions for your reports are given by the director of recreation.

9. Please replace all play equipment in cabinets before the children's meal hours. The head nurse will keep workers informed as to the routine ward work which requires dovetailing with play.

10. On no occasion should workers enter wards or sections of wards where "special precaution" signs are in use. Under no circumstances should play equipment be given to a child who is on "special precaution."

11. The nurse should be consulted before giving anything to a child who is restrained.

12. DIRECT HANDLING OF THE CHILDREN SHOULD BE AVOIDED.

13. Materials and toys dropped on the floor must not be picked up and used before they are cleansed as they are contaminated.

14. No comments regarding patients should be made in the presence of any child.

15. Gifts directly from the volunteer to the children are not encouraged. If any volunteer wants to make some contribution for the whole ward, the recreation director will be glad to give suggestions.

16. Candy or anything to eat must be O.K.'d in advance by the Diet and Nursing Departments.

17. Permission for parties for the children is granted by the hospital when approved by the Medical Departments.

18. Do not visit other parts of the hospital without permission from the Training School Office.

Play in the Education of Nurses

Several small hospitals are affiliated with The Children's Memorial Hospital for the purpose of giving their student nurses experience in nursing children. Its School of Pediatric Nursing offers both academic courses and experience in the wards to meet the needs of two types of students: a four-month course for affiliate students, and one covering six months for graduate nurses, many of whom have been head nurses in other children's hospitals. Among the required subjects for both groups is an introductory course in play for all students, and an additional advanced course for the graduate nurses.

During the period from March, 1932, to December, 1937, 1,004 affiliate and 77 graduate nurses from various parts of the United States and Canada had courses in play in this hospital. Because the type of play that can be carried on without material equipment is especially suited to the hospital situation, it was included for all nurses. Such play can be used by the nurse while giving routine physical care and when the time at her disposal is too limited to permit her to distribute and put away equipment. This particular type of play is well suited to children on precaution and to those newly admitted to the hospital since it makes unnecessary the passing of equipment from one sick child to another.

Because so many activities of this type call for social co-operation they make for harmony and happy relationships among children strange to each other. They also give those children habituated to playthings an opportunity to learn that fun is not dependent upon equipment.

Our records show that most of the student nurses have had very little experience of any sort with children, or when they have it has been very limited. Their training in nursing has stressed physical care, yet they are expected to know how to deal understandingly with the children of all ages from tiny babes to and including adolescents. Their own play experience and attitudes are colored by the competitive types of play that high schools and colleges offer, such as basketball and hockey, or the sports like tennis, archery, or swimming, most of which are unsuitable to young children and certainly to convalescent children. The social, group types of play are rarely offered as college courses in the study of human relationships.

Courses of play had to be framed that would be practical for use in the hospital and have educational value to those enrolled in them. Furthermore, the activities chosen had to be fun and give satisfaction to the students, otherwise the players would have little understanding of the values in those activities and little incentive to share them with their patients. The purpose in giving the courses in play was to acquaint the nurses and volunteer play leaders with the many types of play that children enjoy and to give them some practice in those activities suited to the hospital situation. Naturally, participation in these brief courses was not sufficient to develop the participants into competent play leaders.

THE INTRODUCTORY COURSE IN PLAY. This course included such games as sense, intellectual, singing, and folk games; stories, poetry and nursery rhymes; dramatic play; tricks and puzzles; tongue twisters; codes and sign language; and dramatizing stories and songs. Instead of the usual lecture method, the class work consisted of actually playing games, singing, telling stories, etc. and thereby led the students to the discovery of their values. Practically all student nurses were found to be lacking in any knowledge of the types of play that children enjoy. At first, they seemed self-conscious and ill at ease in this new field that required spontaneity, initiative, and attention to human relationships. The class work led them, step by step, not only in developing skill in playing but in gaining the power to play in a natural, spontaneous way with the children on their wards. They learned to observe the children's behavior and to record their observations in written reports.

Because they shared in what was admittedly an experiment and because they knew from the first day of their attendance in the play class that no grades nor examinations were to be given in this course, the student nurses were induced to express their opinions frankly.

The notion prevalent among many nurses seemed to be that play is beneath the dignity of adults and is intended solely for children. The course in play together with their experiences on the wards changed many of the nurses' attitudes not only toward play but toward children also, and even toward their work. The very fact that for many nurses this was their first experience with children made more vivid everything that was done. The very brevity of their stay made many of those who expected to continue working with children realize the necessity of getting all they could in play activities. No longer was play regarded merely as an amusement or as a convenient tool for keeping the children quiet. Play gave them new ability for meeting trying situations, a new vision and a new understanding of their patients. Nursing is serious business and is full of distressing human problems and monotonous routine. With little knowledge of children's play, one finds it difficult to appreciate how play may prevent many of the very problems that require so much attention from the nurses. That the students realized the value of play for better understanding of their patients is revealed in the following excerpts from their written reports:

"One learns a great deal about children by playing with them. They relax and are their natural selves during play more than at any other time. They seem to enjoy group games more than the individual ones, and it is interesting to watch their dispositions seem to change, sometimes slowly and at other times immediately. To take an active part in children's play gives one a challenging desire to be more alert and helpful to every child's mental growth as well as physical care and to keep him happy and contented. A most striking instance is that of the homesick youngster. By the time he has cried an hour or so for his mother, his temperature has shot up and he is in a nervous, panicky state. Not all the medical knowledge at her command will aid the nurse here, but play, something to take the child's mind off the distressing thing which harasses him, will do that very thing. I think the Recreational Therapy course is one of the most worthwhile things offered us. It makes the nurse better equipped to care for sick individuals."

"Play is the best way to obtain a better understanding of the real child with whom you are working. One Saturday night at 10:30 o'clock we were rushed and very tired when little Orville was admitted to the ward. He was screaming rebelliously, calling for his mother. The doctor came immediately and dressed the child's eye, which had been seriously lacerated. It was necessary to cover the uninjured eye, too, so when the doctor left the room I was alone with a mightily terrified little boy who would have somehow to be bathed. For a few seconds I was almost afraid of the situation and thought to cover my fear with impatience. But as I proceeded quietly with the bath the story of 'Little Black Sambo' came to my rescue and together we put Orville to bed, not as an unmanageable, dirty, little boy, but as a little lad who would soon show his better self to everyone. Incidentally, through this bit of play as I bathed the child, I discovered that his mother had acquainted him with a number of fine stories, that he had many books and that 'mother loved books too, but she could not afford to buy many, that daddy was out of work so they couldn't have pancakes like 'Little Black Sambo,' but daddy knew how to cook beans which were very good for little boys.' So I'm sure that without this little period of play, I would have fought my way through the bath and put Orville to bed as just another bad little boy."

Many examples could be quoted showing how play experiences changed the attitudes of the nurses, but two will suffice to illustrate:

"Since I attended play class I have reformed my attitude toward play and now realize how important it is in the early and fundamental education of a child. I learn through play how to know each child personally and can study the psychological reactions and intelligence of each. The child discovers that the nurse is really a human being. Some forms of play encourage learning of songs, stories, poems. Reason, alertness, accuracy and patience are developed. It exercises the senses of touch, sight and hearing. In all it constitutes a very large and essential part of education."

"I have never been particularly interested in children although I have had a good deal of experience with them and it was surprising to me, during the course, how much more interesting children became when viewed from the angle of their play. It seems to be their world of business, and really they show intelligence, forethought, and executive ability, when given the opportunity. Then it is seasoned with their keen imagination and originality. Adults can learn much by studying children in their play."

Nurses have special need of play. Some nurses claim:

"My maxim is more recreational therapy. A nurse worn to a point of distress by hospital work, welcomes an opportunity to play games. If she has played games formerly, she thinks fondly of her previous experiences, and reminiscing, finds new games. The girl who hasn't played finds herself drawn into them, intrigued by their seeming aimlessness. A nurse who sleeps, eats, works, and makes friends in the hospital atmosphere, reacts enthusiastically to playing. No one but a nurse can realize how these 'idiotic' games give relief from the 'ills' of nursing. Besides mental relaxation, we can see emotional changes. A nurse not only has a fresh uniform but a fresh face as well. She forgets her cares completely, and her worries that perhaps her work is not up to par, or that she may flunk a class. It makes for an atmosphere of congeniality among the girls. Knowing each other better they are not so apt to have personality clashes."

"During my two months' work here I found play to be of great value. My wards have been easier to handle, happier, and the children really contented. Not only have I found it of value here, but also with my friends and my two little cousins. Every week they wait for me to come down and play some new games with them and their school friends."

ADVANCED WORK FOR GRADUATE NURSES. Graduate nurses specializing in pediatrics were admitted for training in January and in June each year, in groups ranging in number from five to twelve. They realized the value of comprehensive training in rounding out their own experience and in meeting the needs of their own hospitals, especially when they had definite jobs awaiting them.

These nurses were given an advanced course in play and a week of experience on the wards during which they devoted their entire time on duty to play with the children under the supervision of the director of play. They learned more of the theory and practice of play, how to make their own play equipment from materials available in a hospital, and they gained a knowledge of children's literature, music, and creative art. They were given experience in demonstrating play activities to parents and in setting up for their inspection small displays of play equipment suitable for children in a hospital.

The nurses used play to meet different needs peculiar to the medical, surgical and orthopedic wards, and to heart, nephritic, and chorea patients, as well as to the children in the convalescent wards. They gave special attention to patients newly admitted, to children about to undergo operations and to those on precaution or in isolation. Over and over, they reported that their most vivid realization of the value of play was playing with children prior to minor operations, when many were filled with fears and dread of the unknown in this, their first hospital experience. For most nurses, although this was their first attempt at playing with a large group of children who were not ill, they were able to successfully apply the principles of group leadership on a larger scale than was possible in the wards.

In cases of major operations the nurses saw the value of play with children, some of whom had undergone one or more operations as hospital patients. The three following excerpts from their reports show that these nurses, like the others, frankly revealed their attitudes:

"My whole experience in play has been of great value to me. I realize in a general way just how it is carried on at this hospital. I have an idea of how much the children enjoy it, and how they look forward to their play from day to day. Regardless of the type of games and materials one takes to them, they soon become absorbed. One always gets some of the following remarks: 'Are you playing in our ward today?' 'Thanks for coming to play with us.' 'Don't forget to come back tomorrow and when you do, bring this game back.' "

"Before I enrolled in play class, I thought all these games were too childish for me. Then I realized they made me relax and get enjoyment and that some required thought on my part. Play has given me some very important ideas that I can use in contacts with children. Although the children's ward in my hospital is small, I will be able to make the children happier by taking their minds off their illnesses. After playing I found that the children liked me better. All children while playing seemed to treat each other nicer."

"Besides putting into practice what I learned in play class, I became familiar with many interesting and amazing stories and games. I learned to present these in an interesting way so that the youngsters wanted to know them too. I learned to shed my self-consciousness outside the ward door and go in and relax with the children. No amount of smoothing of covers and fluffing pillows has ever brought me the exalted feeling that I had when I hushed the continuous crying of a homesick two-year-old with a single finger play. No matter how much discontentment and pain there is in a ward, there is always a visible brightening with the appearance of the 'play lady!' Every child immediately relaxes and has a good time. It was a never ending source of amazement to me to see the absorption in games of the most frightened child. The most valuable thing I acquired was a sense of ease with children. It is something no amount of physical attention has taught me and it is directly due to this week of play."

As the first meeting of a graduate course in play came to a close, a nurse remarked:

"Oh, I *like* this class, I wish we could have it every day. Too bad nurses don't have an hour of play each day to break the strain."

Another commented in her written report:

"After our classes in play I thought I was fairly well equipped to go on my week of concentrated play on the wards. At the end of the week I realized the need of knowing more games, stories, songs, puzzles, riddles, and tricks. The week gave me more opportunity to observe the children than I had before. Some of the things I noted were: how strictly children observed the rules and played fairly, each child taking his turn and accepting the correction of other children; that all the children were more radiant, eager and interested while playing. Group play seems to be an early preparation for community life."

SPECIAL SESSIONS. In addition to the required courses in play, extra sessions were held from time to time for groups of staff and student nurses. Throughout each year demonstrations of play were also given on the wards by the play director and other professionally educated play leaders. Subjects not taught in the regular classes were introduced to the nurses and emphasis was placed on the use of such materials as could be substituted for the more expensive commercially made play equipment.

Epidemics and quarantine sometimes put an abrupt stop to group play by eliminating play leaders entirely from certain wards, and threw the entire responsibility for play upon the nurses there. Even in ordinary circumstances there were children on precaution, or isolation, and no equipment was allowed to be passed from one child to another. Various types of illnesses and stages of convalescence had their special needs. Children on the heart wards, for instance, were not allowed exciting games or those that involved much physical activity. They were the cardiac, nephritic, and the chorea (St. Vitus Dance) patients whose illnesses tend to make them hyperactive. During the first days of their stay in the hospital chorea patients were kept flat on their backs and in restraints as a help in quieting this hyperactivity. These three types needed interesting play that would make them feel they were having what normal children had, but which would not overstimulate nor fatigue them in any way.

To meet these needs, special classes or play clinics were held for the nurses in order that the children might not be deprived of fun even when under strict isolation. The Recreation Office became the teaching center for groups and individuals. Demonstrations of possible play were also given on the wards.

STAFF EDUCATION IN PLAY. Our aim was to give the staff nurses in an introductory course of play some inkling of the re-creative values of play and of the joy in playing. The first series of practical demonstrations of play requiring no material equipment was given three Monday evenings, starting September 27, 1933. Forty of the staff attended. One serious and very competent nurse said that never in her life had she played such simple games and laughed so much.

The second series was given once each month during the first four months of 1937. The main effort was directed to acquainting one-third of the old and all of the new staff, who had had no experience, with this kind of play. In addition, 13 night and relief nurses had the regular Beginners' Class of eight lessons in play, and 27 had the advanced class of eight additional lessons.

EDUCATION IN PLAY EMPHASIZES THE IMPORTANCE OF THE HUMAN ELEMENTS IN NURSING. The whole experience in play helped the student nurse to become better oriented in her new profession. To the student, plunged into such subjects as psychology, mental hygiene, psychiatry, and child development with their bewildering vocabularies, play revealed child behavior daily and hourly in a form she could understand and deal with immediately and effectively. Play created the situation which vivified abstract theories, gave meaning and definiteness to many concepts that might otherwise have been vague and meaningless to the student nurse. Moreover, understanding better what she is dealing with, the nurse feels obligated to treat problems constructively, because she is made to realize that, neglected, the child may be retarded or otherwise handicapped.

Education in play tends to make the children interesting personalities to the nurse; she no longer is so likely to single out the particularly attractive child as the object of her special attention. Instead, she begins to see the possibilities of aiding any so-called "problem child" to develop the more attractive aspects of his personality by means of play.

It became increasingly apparent to the nurses that through play many an unpleasant issue could be avoided entirely by offering the child activities which stimulated his potentialities and gave them orderly expression. It became apparent also that the child might be prevented from passing over into the problem class, thereby necessitating exhaustive diagnosis and extensive psychiatric treatment.

The Education of Parents in the Selection of Play Materials

DISPLAYS OF PLAY MATERIALS AND DEMONSTRATIONS OF PLAY. During the period from 1932 to 1938, approximately ninety-seven per cent of the children in the hospital were charity patients, paying nothing or only a small part of the expenses. Although for the most part their relatives had very little money to spend, they often brought gifts to the children, many of which were unsuitable for a hospital patient and of which the children soon tired.

In an effort to stem this weekly tide of shoddy, unsuitable or even dangerous toys, the supervising nurse on duty in the admitting room checked the gifts brought in and explained why this or that particular gift was unsuitable. Such explanations, though reasonable to the hospital staff, often appeared quite the contrary to the visitors, many of whom had come long distances and gone out of their way to buy the gift that the hospital of necessity refused to permit the child to have.

A more constructive method was decided upon in March, 1934. Because most of the parents were so poor, it was decided to display more worthwhile games and toys that could be bought at little expense or could even be made from materials found in their homes. These exhibits, though limited, were planned to meet the particular needs of the children, including different types of illnesses and with due regard to actual conditions on the wards. To insure originality in planning the displays, all the supervisors and student nurses participating in the experiment were required to work together and to share the results of their experiences on the wards. This kept them alert in discovering new play materials, inventive in the making of play equipment, and watchful of the children's reactions.

The play director conferred each Friday morning with the two nurses assigned to arrange the display for the following afternoon on visitors' day. Attention was given not only to the selection of suitable materials but also to their attractive arrangement on the four-wheeled cart provided for the purpose.

On Saturday afternoons the nurses presented the displays, with explanations for parents and other adult visitors, in the dispensary. Following the display in the dispensary, a part of the exhibit was set up in the waiting room of the hospital, where it remained for one week.

EDUCATIONAL VALUE OF THE DISPLAYS AND DEMONSTRATIONS. A steady growth of interest in the displays was shown by the visitors. In April, 1934, a nurse's report read as follows:

"The toys brought in have been improving. We received only five 'hazards' and two of them were from the same visitor. When the mothers first came, they hurried by and didn't seem much interested. Later, some stopped and inquired if they could buy the toys, but we told them they were suggestions of things that could be bought in the stores, for ten cents, and that they were good presents to bring. Many of the books and toys the visitors brought were suggested by those we had previously had on display."

One graduate nurse displayed articles such as blunt scissors, crayolas, pencils, paper and paste, all of which children find useful while in a hospital, but which few parents ever thought of bringing them. She reported an enthusiastic reception of her games and stories, "but as far as the display was concerned, I considered it a failure." The next visitors' day another nurse reported:

"It was interesting to note the impression the previous display had made. Scissors, crayolas, paste, etc., had been shown and very few parents came today without one of these articles. One father told the nurse he had gone to three different stores before he found a bottle of paste exactly like the one shown last week."

Setting up these displays proved valuable training for the nurses in charge of them. Here on a small, easily comprehended scale they learned to select play equipment intelligently, to arrange it attractively, and to observe and record the reactions of the visitors.

DEMONSTRATIONS OF PLAY. In addition to improvement in the type of gifts brought to the children, there was also a change in the attitude of visitors toward the hospital. Irritability over the necessarily long waits in the dispensary and antagonism aroused by the hospital's refusal to accept hazardous playthings was lessened through the parents' participation in demonstrations of play activities that children enjoy.

Many of the parents had to bring their other children with them when they came to visit their sick child. Since it was the rule of the hospital that a ward patient be allowed but one visitor at a time and that no one under seventeen years of age was allowed to visit patients, the younger children were often subjected to long waits in the dispensary. They created a problem and at the same time an opportunity. In 1936, a graduate nurse who had had the advanced course in play took this opportunity to experiment with demonstrations of play with these children and with the adult relatives of the patients. She reports the circumstances in which the demonstrations were initiated:

"One mother approached very timidly and asked if she might look at our exhibit. She thought it most interesting and liked 'Symbola' particularly. A father was interested in 'Fish Pond.' 'Do you know, I'd like to play this myself,' he said. One little boy stood near watching intently. Finally he said, 'Gee, these are swell games for kids. Do you play these in the hospital?' Knowing that the target game could be washed, I hit upon the plan of letting the children show their parents just how it was played. They had the time of their lives. Many fathers and mothers enjoyed the sport. At four o'clock they were loath to leave. The oldest boy ventured to ask, 'Will you be here again next Saturday?' I felt like a Pied Piper as they followed me to the elevator."

Supervising the play of the waiting children was good experience for the nurses, because they could make practical application of the games and other activities, and test the theories learned in their classes, with children in a more normal situation than work with the patients in the hospital afforded. The following reports show both the nurses' and visitors' attitudes toward these displays and demonstrations:

"This was one of the most profitable afternoons I have ever spent. At first the visiting children were shy, but soon all joined in the fun, even an overgrown eleven-year-old boy who said he was too old for such games. They were interested in the display and said they wished they had such games to play with. (Inexpensive checkers, anagrams, bird lotto, bowls, etc.) They enjoyed all the games. Many mothers, attracted by the singing and laughing, came over to watch the fun. We had a hard time playing 'My Father Keeps a Grocery Store,' for the mothers insisted on guessing before the children had a chance. Two mothers asked about hospital play, and when they understood how games were adapted, they were surprised and pleased. One said, 'I'll never worry about my boy again. They don't overlook anything in this hospital.' One little boy asked if we played all these games with the sick children. When told we did he said, 'Gee, I don't see why I can't get sick like my brother.' "

"The clock pointed to 1:30 p.m. as I opened the elevator door of the dispensary and pushed out the cart that contained suggested Christmas gifts for hospitalized children. The display aroused the enthusiasm of the waiting parents and I was hardly able to put the cart in place before it was surrounded. I explained the advantages of each gift.

"But a ten-year-old girl was tugging at my arm. 'Aren't you going to play with us? Let's play this, I'll bet it's fun.' We were joined immediately by the girls, an eleven-year-old boy, a five-year-old girl and a boy of seven. I left the older ones playing together and played ball with the younger ones. Soon there were more boys and girls. They all seemed interested in the games on display. We played bowling during which much enthusiasm developed. The 'Playwoodies' provided entertainment for the older children as well as for those about six years old. Every time a child made an object, he brought it joyfully over for my approval. Puzzle peg intrigued the older ones, as did 'Finishing Squares.'

"Twelve children were now in the party, one a toddler twenty months old. 'How would you like to play ball?' I asked. The grip on his father's hand tightened so I gave the ball to the father who played eagerly with his son. I went back to the others. Soon the father said, 'Could you sell this ball?' I said it was impossible but that a ball of the same sort could be purchased for ten cents. The mother later joined in the play while the father visited their child in the hospital."

"Each time a new child joined the group and I asked, 'Would you like to play with us?' he would act backward but as soon as he learned the fundamentals of the game he was no longer a stranger but an enthusiastic youngster apparently perfectly at ease. What power play has!"

"The reading of the Christmas story by an older girl proved of great interest to some of the children who sat wide-eyed as she read. The younger children were bubbling with energy and could not keep still. Playing ball gave them satisfaction. Being able to catch first with both hands, then with the right, and next with the left was a splendid accomplishment. I glanced at the clock and was surprised to find it a quarter of four. I had no idea it was so late. Mentally I observed, 'Play *is* certainly marvelous.' And it is not only for children, for I observed the interest displayed by the parents, and my own absorption made me realize how much concentration play affords. I told the children I had to leave. Very coöperatively they helped to gather all the articles, signal the elevator, and assist in getting the cart in. 'I'd certainly like to be in this hospital. Oh, but it must be fun here,' I heard one little girl say. They stood waving in a body as I closed the elevator door. 'You'll be coming again?' they asked. 'Someone will be here to play next time,' I assured them."

"How easy it is to become a child's friend with play—indispensable play! I had a marvelously enjoyable afternoon and believe the children had too. I put the display articles in the visitors' waiting room, thinking of my afternoon's experiences and feeling grateful for being allowed to enjoy such an entirely different program. I could but realize anew and appreciate again the great value of play in our hospital. Surely every moment spent in play is a moment well spent. I count the afternoon as an invaluable experience."

CHAPTER 4

PLAY ACTIVITIES AND THEIR USE

THE PROBLEM OF RETARDATION. At present, available facts are insufficient to determine either the cause or extent of retardation among children. The seriousness of their problem, however, is indicated by the number of retarded crippled children alone, in the United States. In 1930, the Committee on the Physically and Mentally Handicapped reported, in the White House Conference on Child Health and Protection, that a study of three thousand crippled children in special schools showed that "75 per cent are over aged, 22 per cent are of average age, and .017 per cent are under aged chronologically." [1]

Also, this committee stressed the fact that the needs of handicapped children are "the common needs of all children," but by the nature of their weaknesses they require greater attention to their physical, mental, emotional, and social needs than do the normally well children. The committee showed further that to meet these needs the children must be considered as totalities.

Not only the physical condition, but the mental viewpoints and attitudes of the crippled child should be given consideration in administering treatment. Every effort should be made to discover his potential abilities and to give him

1. Committee on Physically and Mentally Handicapped. White House Conference on Child Health and Protection, Sec. IV. *The Handicapped Child,* p. 144. New York, Century (1933).

the use of all the powers he has in order to compensate for his handicap and to enable him to achieve success in spite of it.

If in their treatment of these children the fields of medicine, psychiatry, social work, nursing, and education were integrated, better results would no doubt be attained in both the prevention and cure of retardation. Obviously, integrated treatment is quite different from merely adding together what the doctor, the psychiatrist, the social worker, and the teacher recommend for the child.

If, in the hospital, the various educational efforts as well as the medical treatment of the handicapped child were in themselves something more of an integration process it, too, might help to prevent retardation. But this cannot be done merely by providing school teachers for the purpose of keeping patients abreast of their school grades, for such efforts meet the children's needs only partially. No doubt there are many children that are retarded because long periods of illness have not only kept them from the formal education provided by the schools, but also from the informal education they might normally have had in school, home, and community social associations.

It has been found that some of these omissions in the child's informal education can be supplied by a stimulating program of play including more activities that serve at once to release and integrate the child's latent powers. Almost invariably by our academic teaching methods we set up too many barriers to free action by selecting one aspect of an activity and arbitrarily shutting out others that would function were spontaneity encouraged. In general the treatment of academic subject matter is of necessity confined too exclusively to the word level to stimulate sub-verbal behavior in the child. Play, on the contrary, enables the child to function intelligently on sub-verbal levels through the free exercise of the senses and muscular activity. Moreover, play is an effective medium for enabling the child to organize and focus his resources for successful achievement. This is integration. It is the omission of just such activities that causes blockages—another name for some types of retardation.

Custom, precedent, routine, and concentration on disease have produced a cultural lag in many children's hospitals. It is typical of all professions dealing with children that practice lags far behind known facts. Whereas eminent authorities in the fields of biology, psychology, art, and education advocate play as one of the most vital elements in child development, few hospital boards and administrators have provided adequately for it in their care of child patients.

PLAY AND THE ARTS A NECESSITY IN EDUCATION. Education by means of play restores that unity of mind and body that traditional teaching methods tend to disrupt. Play, rather than formal teaching, appears to be a method more 'natural' to the child because it enables him to learn and to express with his whole body. So many of the most vital experiences of childhood are below word level, capable of expression only in action and feeling. Eastman claims that children, like poets, are enthusiastic about the intrinsic qualities, the essences of things. They seek the pleasures of experiencing all the qualities—not just the abstract one by which a thing is named—and they want to experience these in body as well as in mind. Our usual education "takes from them their many-colored world," dulls their imagination, prevents initiative, and blocks creative expression.[2]

Jacks, former principal of Manchester College, Oxford,

2. Eastman, Max, *Enjoyment of Poetry*, pp. 6-45, New York, Scribner (1928).

believes that the usual education given in schools is super-
ficial, unassimilated, and disconnected from the personality
of the student. Denied creative activity, a body is thwarted
"in the very core and essence of its nature. And because
thwarted, unhealthy." [3] Dewey calls play a "moral necessity." [4] Seashore goes even further by stating, "With the
deeper significance discovered in play, comes a broader in-
terpretation of education, knowledge, morality, art, and
religion." [5]

Play appears to be in accordance with the child's own interest and with the suggestions of modern science. Learning
is a function of the body as a whole in what is called by
Coghill [6] a total pattern or, by Child, [7] an organismic process.
The neurological researches of Cannon [8] and Coghill sub-
stantiate this general point of view. Modern science recog-
nizes in play the constructive values of interest and joy.
Jennings considers these two elements responsible for un-
hindered, flourishing development and harmonious functioning, whereas worry, fear, and unhappiness he regards as
indications of blockage. He states:

"The young child perhaps learns more and develops better
through its play than through any other form of activity. Opportunity for varied play under healthful outward conditions is

3. Jacks, Lawrence Pearsall, *Education Through Recreation*, p. 87, New
   York, Harpers (1932).
4. Dewey, John, *The Philosophy of John Dewey* (Ed. by Ratner), p. 499,
   New York, Holt (1928); *Human Nature and Conduct*, pp. 159-164,
   New York, Holt (1932).
5. Seashore, Carl Emil, *Psychology in Daily Life*, p. 1, New York,
   Appleton (1913).
6. Coghill, G. E., "The Structural Basis of the Integration of Behavior,"
   Proceedings National Academy of Science (1930).
7. Child, C. M., *Physiological Foundations of Behavior*, New York, Longmans, Green (1924).
8. Cannon, Walter B., *Bodily Changes in Pain, Hunger, Fear and Rage*,
   New York, Appleton (1929).

beyond doubt the chief need of children; comparative study of the mental and physical development of children to whom full opportunity for such play is given shows striking superiority, as compared with children to whom such opportunities are denied." [9]

That group play can reach depths untouched by the traditional school methods has been demonstrated by Bertha E. Schlotter [10, 11] in the State School and Colony, an institution for the mentally deficient located at Lincoln, Illinois, and by Florence Beaman Bock [12] in The Little Red School House of New York City. Miss Schlotter's achievements in using group play with the mentally deficient patients ranging in chronological age from two to sixty-five years, included five classifications. About half the number had been considered educable. Some of the imbeciles and idiots had the additional handicap of being hopelessly crippled and yet it was demonstrated that many of these were educable to a greater degree than the staff psychologists had thought possible.

Mrs. Bock's work with delinquent and so-called incorrigible boys in the Montefiore Special School in Chicago and with the mentally superior unadjusted children in New York are two examples of the success of group play methods.

9. Jennings, H. S., "The Biology of Children in Relation to Education." *Suggestions of Modern Science Concerning Education,* p. 43, New York, Macmillan (1921).

10. Schlotter, B. E., "Education Through Play." Program of the Mental Hygiene Division of the Illinois Conference of Public Welfare, Chicago (October, 1933). Obtainable from Ethel Dummer, 679 North Michigan Ave., Chicago, Illinois.

11. Schlotter, B. E. and M. Svendsen, "Experiment in Recreation with the Mentally Deficient." Obtainable from the State School, Lincoln, Illinois, and from The Institute of Juvenile Research, 907 South Lincoln St., Chicago, Illinois.

12. Accounts of the methods used by Mrs. Bock may be found in Readers Guide (1924, 1926, 1932, 1933).

PLAY FOR THE CRIPPLED CHILDREN. There are many types of physical conditions by which children are classified as cripples. Each type and each child should be treated as unique in determining the kind and the amount of play to be given. Physically active crippled children may be given many of the games and play activities that normal children indulge in, provided the activity be gauged to their handicap. Dramatic play, puppetry, group singing and story telling, group and individual projects in the arts, crafts and construction, rhythm bands and playing musical instruments, gardening, and many types of nature study may be used as play. While a great variety of activities may be used, the selection must be made with due regard to their condition and to the restrictions of casts, braces, and wheel chairs. Traditional non-musical games, folk and singing games, various target, table, and board games, are often suitable for crippled children. To these may be added, for outdoor play, croquet, miniature golf, and games involving bowling and throwing. All the "social" types of play can be used with results beneficial mentally, physically, and emotionally, especially when played in the outdoor air and sunshine.

PLAY FOR THE RESTRICTED PATIENT. Heart and chorea cases and tubercular patients are likely to have, at times, an overwhelming sense of inferiority. The play of these children should be varied and progressively more difficult, in order to induce whatever improvement is possible, especially for those who must have months and years of hospital care. As pleasant changes from handcrafts or busy-work and too much reading and listening to stories, they may play many games that involve but little physical action. They must have the quieting types of play because the very nature of their diseases tends to make them easily excited and hyperactive.

A play program for them should be a definite and carefully planned part of the care of all handicapped children, particularly of that type of heart case in which seemingly trifling emotional disturbances are more likely to produce shock than is physical exertion. If play is a part of the daily program, and if games are given frequently for short periods of time, they can be effective in calming over-active children. Such children give themselves readily to the self-discipline which games impose upon the participants. When well selected and supervised, singing games, in particular, produce happiness, buoyancy, and orderliness.

Instances of using effectively very simple games on the heart ward are reported by two student nurses:

1. "When on the heart ward I was able to play a great deal and we looked forward to our minutes of play. There were eleven boys in all, each with a different temperament—quiet, shy, grumbly, tough—but we did seem to get along together and usually all participated in the games 'Going to New York,' 'ABC,' 'Bird Game.' At times one or two were teasing or bullying a younger child and really quarreling as I entered the room. These feelings were all gone when we played games and an atmosphere of sportsmanship and pleasure prevailed."

2. "Group play lends harmony to the wards and instills friendliness in antagonistic groups. Ward 2 harbored eight fussy, irritable girls, four of them chorea patients. On this particular day I was unable to get any one of them to speak politely to another. After half an hour I decided to do something. I began with 'I See Something So Big and So Tall.' Within five minutes Ward 2 was the quietest and most harmonious on the floor."

Play with Patients
Before Surgical Operations

PLAY BEFORE MINOR OPERATIONS. Experiments over a period of approximately six years have proved that group play is efficacious in lessening fears and diverting attention when the child is about to undergo such operations as those for tonsils and adenoids, usually termed minor, but sometimes so terrorizing as to affect children emotionally for years. For many children this first experience in the hospital is also their first night away from home. Many of them come with strange fears of doctors, nurses, and hospital—fears that are magnified by the odor of ether, by the sight of nurses coming from the operating rooms looking like ghosts in their all-white garb and masks, and by the doctors wearing queer instruments around their necks and foreheads. The cries of other children, breaking in upon the strange, tense quiet, add to their fears. Children are calmed somewhat by knowing the steps in their treatment: that they will have baths, be put to bed, be awakened early, etc., but the very words doctors and nurses use in trying to explain away their fears tend to conjure up frightening pictures in their minds. For instance, after a nurse had said, "The doctor will give you a 'stick' in the arm," a boy was found tightly clutching a wooden tongue depressor. Asked what he was going to do with it, he said, "It's the stick for the doctor to use in my arm." Sometimes the expression used is "a shot in the arm," and nurses have on occasions observed a look of fear sweep from face to face—a shot being associated with quite other matters than the prick of a needle. Many children regard illness as a punishment for some wrong they have done, and doctors and nurses as agents for punishing them. The expression on the face of an over-imaginative child is alone sufficient to infect a whole group with fears that may grow fantastic to overwhelming proportions.

In facilitating favorable conditioning in the children, play has proved a most effective instrument. The mere fact that someone had time to play with them was reassuring. Like a stranger in a foreign land, who suddenly hears his own language, the child reaches out to play as an assurance of friendliness in a bewildering situation.

Experiments in play immediately preceding operations were begun in June, 1932. By December of that year, this had become an established procedure welcomed by doctors, nurses, and children. The superintendent reported that the children were taking the anesthetic quietly and that "recovery afterwards is noticeably more tranquil, as compared with the pandemonium which used to characterize tonsil day." [13]

Monday, Wednesday, and Friday mornings, between eight and ten o'clock, usually found from nine to fifteen patients ranging from two to thirteen years of age, waiting for tonsil and adenoid operations. At eight o'clock these children were assembled on a small sun porch as far from the operating room as possible. Nurses came at intervals of from five to twenty minutes, taking first the youngest children for operations and then the older ones, who might have to wait two hours or longer for their turn—a longer period of time than children would be expected to play in ordinary circumstances. Therefore, the games chosen had not only to appeal to a wide age range, but to be so absorbing as to hold the interest of many of the children over a long period of waiting and in spite of constant interruptions. Furthermore, the children must not be overstimulated or unduly fatigued. Since the

13. Binner, Mabel W., "They Play with You Here," *The Modern Hospital*, Vol. 44, p. 58. St. Louis, The Modern Hospital Publishing Co. (February, 1935).

space was far too limited and had to accommodate as many as fifteen children, as well as the examining doctors, the nurses, and the play director, the selection of the games was of necessity determined to a certain extent by these governing factors. The types of play best adapted to the total problem had to be determined by experimentation with many kinds of games and with many groups. One outstanding phase of the problem was the selection of play activities that made the strongest appeal to the children and held their interest under unfavorable conditions.

Play usually began with one or two singing games. The children reacted as though they thought a hospital where one sang and played games could not be such a bad place after all. Folk games, such as "While Traveling Over Sea and Land," or "Adam's Sons," appealed to boys and girls ranging in age from two to thirteen years. Girls like "Thorn Rosa," "A Walk in the Moonlight," and the littlest ones enjoyed "Here Comes a Bluebird." When an interne came to check teeth, throats, and chests, a target or bowling game, or "Bean Bag Board" with sides competing and the children seated in two lines, fitted in nicely because the games and the examinations could proceed without interfering with each other.

Since the youngest children were taken first it proved less distracting if the children were divided into two groups according to age range. They might be seated around two tables for playing such games as "Fish Pond," or one of the Lotto games, since these appealed to children of various ages. After a game or two with the group, the younger children were usually given free play with peg or form boards. Sense games such as "Mrs. Santa," "Mind Reading," "I See Red," "Magic Three," and the like proved useful since they appealed to most of the children. The interest of the older children was held to the last by such games as "Five in a Row," "Hang a Man," "Color Cubes," "Mosaics," "Puzzle Peg," and stick tricks.

That the children enjoyed their play is evidenced by such spontaneous outbursts as "Gee, these are swell games!" "Are they neat!" "My, but we have fun here!" One day a little colored girl darted off the operating table, snatched her shoes and was half way down the hall before the nurse caught up with her to take her back to the operating room. She protested, "I didn't come here to go to sleep. I came to play games." A ten-year-old girl remarked, "I'd just as soon stay here forever. We have more fun here than we do at home." Games of the "social" type played with the children were apparently especially appealing. "I wish we had games like these in school," said a boy of eleven. "Don't you have games at school?" he was asked. "Oh, we have baseball, volley ball, and things like that, but no games," he replied. Several boys from various schools expressed agreement with him in wishing they had games of this type at school.

PLAY WITH NEWLY ADMITTED PRIVATE PATIENTS. The usual routine was to have private patients scheduled for tonsil and adenoid operations brought into rooms adjoining the sun porch by 9:30 o'clock on the day of the operation. Many of these children like the ward patients, showed varying degrees of fear even though accompanied by their parents. Each parent was given instructions as to the use of games suited to his own child's age and probable interest. Equipment games and play materials, such as "Fishing," "Peg," "Lotto," target games, color and design blocks, and mosaics, were found effective in diverting the attention of the child distraught with fear, into new channels by presenting an intriguing challenge in the form of a game. Parents often expressed surprise at the skill and concentration required by these games, the rules of which could be grasped quickly. To cite one example: One morning after their children had been taken to the operating room, several parents, who had never seen each other before, became interested in playing table golf together. They were surprised at the way the game held their interest and at the way it helped to make the time pass quickly.

During the year of 1937 alone, ninety parents were shown how to keep their ninety-two children fully occupied and unworried before minor operations. One mother carried her four-year-old boy, sobbing in terror on her shoulder, to watch the two groups of other tonsil and adenoid patients absorbed in play. He stopped crying immediately and played three games very happily, before his turn came to go to the operating room. The mother said she had never seen anything like it and was surprised at the quiet and ease of all the children and the instantaneous effect of play upon her boy. He had had an appendix operation at another hospital where the screaming children had so frightened him that the very word "hospital" seemed to bring back the horror of that experience. Another mother, observing a graduate nurse conduct play with fourteen tonsil patients, remarked, "It's simply wonderful how you know how to handle so many children. I have three and I never know what to do with them all at one time."

PLAY WITH NEWLY ADMITTED WARD PATIENTS. Children admitted for operations showed most fright at the time of admittance and just before the operations. Whereas private patients were brought in on the morning of their tonsil and adenoid operations and their parents waited with them, the other patients scheduled for minor operations were admitted the afternoon before the operation, usually in numbers of from nine to fifteen. Their parents left as soon as the routine of admission was finished, and the children were then taken to their wards. Often their crying and screaming could be heard the full length of the corridors. In their terror some kicked and bit, and the efforts of the nurses to quiet them were often ineffective. The play director decided to experiment with play.

Upon admittance, ward patients were assigned to two rooms of from six to eight beds each. The beds were pushed together temporarily, leaving space at the end of the room for play. The size of the play space, the fact that sick children occupied neighboring rooms, and the doctor's rule forbidding the use of play equipment that would later be circulated among the other patients were factors affecting the choice of play activities.

Singing games were usually suggested by the children themselves, and proved not to be disturbing to the neighboring patients. "Did You Ever See a Lassie," "Farmer in the Dell," "London Bridge," and similar games were popular. Sense games and those of the simple intellectual type, such as "Pretend Hide," "Button Button," "I see Something Red," "Mind Reading," "I Spy," were popular and easily played in small space. Games such as "Black Magic," "Counter Point," "My Grandmother Doesn't Like T," proved particularly attractive to the older children. Because rubber balls could be washed, the children were permitted to bounce or throw a ball into a basket, to play "Teacher," "Bowling into a Circle," and similar games. Story telling, simple dramatic play and puzzles gave variety to the play period. Whenever holidays were celebrated in the hospital with special decorations, games, and refreshments, these newly arrived children, too, had a party.

Permanent equipment on the wards included a radio, a large box of blocks, blackboards and a steel cabinet containing other play material. The children were permitted to use the equipment throughout the day but were expected to put everything in order before meal time.

It was demonstrated again and again that nurses equipped with a working knowledge of play activities were able to bring orderly quiet out of pandemonium. One example will suffice: One August afternoon, the nurses in the admitting room reported that fourteen boys brought in for minor operations were the toughest and most badly behaved they had ever encountered. The pharmacist, whose drug room was opposite the admitting room, said they were noisier than any group she had ever known in the hospital. They tore at the nurses' hands, screamed, bit and kicked. Tact, arguments and coercion, all failed. Reports of the condition sent the director of play in haste to the ward where they had been taken, to help the nurse. Her help was not needed. The quiet little nurse had started play immediately upon the boys' arrival in the ward. She said that two of them were difficult at first but all soon joined in playing "Button Button." A visiting doctor dropped in a little later and commented: "Certainly a well-controlled, contented-looking lot of boys!"

Nurses can be taught to help children face hospital treatment fearlessly when at the onset of fear they see other children with problems similar to their own playing happily. One nurse wrote of a five-year-old girl who was to have tonsils removed:

"She cried so hard she was taken out of the larger ward and put into the smaller room with only four others. Immediately she threw herself on the floor under the bed. When I tried to pick her up she became stiff and tried to scratch. At first it seemed impossible to distract her attention from the idea of going home. After a while she saw the other girls playing. Suddenly she said between sobs, 'What is this little girl crying for? I's all stopped now.' She asked to be taken to the larger ward where she looked at books and played games with the other fourteen girls. By bedtime she had forgotten all about going home. The next morning she was among the most fearless of the younger children who had operations. She didn't cry even when given the hypodermic medication, but played games on the sun porch and seemed quite free from fear when the nurse came to take her to the operating room."

PLAY BEFORE MAJOR OPERATIONS. The orthopedic ward contained five rooms with from two to eight children in each. Here the children were given either individual or group play before being summoned to the operating room. The director made it a point to play with these children on the afternoon before, as well as the morning of their operations. She and the graduate nurses assigned to play gave special attention to the newly admitted patients.

A staff nurse sent by another hospital to observe the method and types of play described her morning of observation:

"First I took part in play with Michael, a five-year-old boy with club feet. We had a fishing game, made by the hospital children, of blocks and small barrel-like articles with screw-hooks in the tops, that represented sacks of gold and silver or jewels down in the bottom of the sea. The fisherman had a pole with a ring at the end of the string. We fished to see who could catch the most valuable sacks, the values being marked on the bottom. Michael couldn't add but it was surprising how he appreciated the fact that 5 and 10 were of much less value than 25 or 50. His eyes gleamed and he knew he was beating when he caught the 100 sack. We played this several times and would have played longer if the cart hadn't come to take him to the operating room. He certainly forgot all about the operation."

"Then I observed a two-year-old, with a T.B. spine, on a frame trying to put squares, rectangles, balls, and eggs of wood into a barrel through the proper holes in the top, and a three-year-old child playing with a color pyramid. In the girls' ward, three beds were moved together around a bedside table and I made a fourth for a game of Symbola. The girls' ages were 14, 10, and 5. They explained the game which resembles dominoes, and appeared quite thrilled. 'Can we play another game before we go to the operating room?' asked one of the girls with such amazing calmness! So we played Stealing Birds, a game like Casino but using packs of bird cards that come in soda boxes. This game stimulates alertness. They recognize the birds by color and shape."

Three nurses give something of a picture of the conditions orthopedic patients often undergo in the course of treatment:

1. "Most of them have had previous operative experience and know what to expect by way of discomfort. Many dread the ordeal. Play is excellent before major operations, and demonstrates its value in relieving the mind of anxiety. The children showed marked enthusiasm. 'Gee, the morning went fast!' said a nine-year-old boy before he went to the operating room. An eight-year-old boy played Puzzle Peg for twenty-five minutes before he went. When he left, he said, 'Gee whiz, I even forgot about myself.' "

2. "A ten-year-old girl, with a spastic paralysis, nervous because of the nature of her condition, went to the operating room calmly because she had been so busy playing she did not have time to dwell upon what was coming. And I can still hear Angela, a twelve-year-old girl, wishing she were going to the operating room because the girls that were going were having so much fun."

3. "Bill, who had had about twenty operations, was quite unconcerned when his twenty-first approached. He was always busy

with his play and his school work. The only comment I heard him make was that the operation wouldn't be bad. He would just have to be on his back for ten days, then he could be up and playing again. In Anna's case, play probably prevented the child from becoming neurotic. After her operations her whole attention was centered on her condition. She was gradually drawn by play of the other children until she took an active part in it."

NEED FOR TRAINED LEADERSHIP BEFORE OPERATIONS. The organization of play before operations, even under the best of conditions, is not easy, however smoothly it may appear to go under the direction of a skillful play leader. It is not a job of amusing or entertaining children by "someone-who-has-a-way-with-children." It demands the best of play leadership, a knowledge of values and how to bring them out, as well as adaptability in emergencies and in meeting children's needs as they arise. Should the doctors be delayed, the nurses be too rushed, the attendants irritable, or a child cry continuously, the children reflect the atmosphere thus created. The group may include a "mama's baby" who feels very sorry for himself because never before has he been without his mother's anxious care. There may be one or more children who have had major operations previously, who still have vivid memories of pain endured, or there may be a child who has never faced pain but has always escaped hard reality in day-dreaming. The child with too vivid imagination may build up a picture, wholly unfounded and grotesquely fantastic, of dreadful conditions ahead. It is difficult to estimate whether the bullying tease who pictures vividly to others what they will face or the highly imaginative child who never says a word, but whose whole countenance and attitude express terror, does the most damage to the other children's morale before the play leader reaches them.

Parents subjected to high emotional strain before their

children's operations can have that tension lessened by taking part in the games with their children, or by merely seeing a group of children engrossed in playing together.

Most administrators of hospitals for children have failed to realize the invaluable service they can give by providing skilled leadership for play. Dr. Brenneman, physician-in-chief of The Children's Memorial Hospital, says, "The reaction of the patient and of his parents is the ultimate yardstick by which a hospital should be measured." He compares hospitals, built to serve the sick and suffering, with commercial enterprises such as the hotel, the store, the movie, and the gasoline station, where every device is used to give better service to their patrons, and asks why a hospital "fails more often to achieve fully its whole purpose." [14]

Since the trained play leader has, in well-selected play, a magic wand for dispersing children's fears, is it not a pity so few hospitals make provision for play before children submit to surgical operations, and that minor operations continue to be regarded as of little consequence in the child's emotional experience? Why are thousands of children subjected to terrors that are preventable? For example, for years an eight-year-old boy had recurring nightmares in which he screamed, "Don't let the nurse get me; keep the doctor away." His need for remedial reading in school led to the discovery of the connection of his inability to read and his emotional conditioning with a previous tonsilectomy.

While thousands of children undergo operations successfully as far as physical health is concerned, there is always the possibility of unfortunate conditioning because of the vividness of the experience. But it must be remembered that

14. Brenneman, Joseph, M.D., "The Human Side of a Hospital." *Journal of the American Medical Association,* Vol. 7, pp. 1487-1489 (November 14, 1931).

not all fears nor conditionings are created in the hospital. The home is also responsible. A study of pre-school children at the Iowa Child Welfare Research Station listed in the order of their prevalence five things feared by pre-school children: (1) dogs, (2) doctors, (3) storms, (4) deep water and (5) darkness. This research also showed that children tend to take on fears similar to those of their mothers.[15]

To prevent these conditionings play was given, before minor operations, to 6,614 ward patients in the Children's Memorial Hospital in the period from June 1932, to December 1937.

The Arts, Crafts and Construction Materials Utilized as Play

MUSIC. Singing was one of the happy experiences of the patients in the hospital. In commenting on its effectiveness, a nurse said:

"There are times in the ward when everything and everyone seems to be on edge. Some jolly little song—even though you cannot sing and may be informed by one of the children that you went up or down at the wrong place—changes the entire atmosphere as one after the other the children join in the singing and forget that Mary across the way has a picture book better and brighter than theirs."

The timbre of the children's voices made it possible for those in one ward to sing without disturbing even very ill patients in the adjoining room.

How the faces of the children born of foreign parentage would light up when some folk song familiar to them was

15. Hagman, Elmer R., "A Study of Fears of Children of Pre-School Age," *Journal of Experimental Education*, Vol. 1, p. 110 (December, 1932).

sung, even though the words were in a language strange to them. Rarely was there a child who did not join in singing when informal methods, such as beginning with a traditional singing game, were followed. Sometimes older boys, newly arrived in the hospital, would be diffident or embarrassed when the group started a song, and would ask, "Do we *have* to sing?" "No, indeed! You may keep still or you may whistle if you'd rather," was the reassuring reply.

Singing soon became one of the accepted activities and children of all ages sang simply and naturally together for their own enjoyment. The absence of a song leader standing before the group and beating time or commenting on values and tone quality left the children free to sing because they enjoyed it. True, the results were not always fine harmony, but the interest and enthusiasm, which the play methods produced, were evident as the children eagerly made their own selections from the songs they knew and even asked to learn new ones.

With the exception of "Animal Crackers" and cow-boy songs heard over the radio, it was interesting to note that few of their choices were songs of the popular type. Some were those composed especially for children, while others were those they had heard adults sing. Among them were the serious, the gay, and the merely nonsensical, or those accompanied by action, or again the accompaniment of a game, all selected according to the mood of the individual or the group. On the various wards, even on Cribside with babies, the nurses experimented with different kinds of songs. They reported instances in which certain songs made the babies "fussy" and even started some to crying, while others, such as Schubert's "Slumber Song" and Brahms' "Lullaby," made them smile and relax. Many of the babies appeared to listen attentively.

One of the board members of the hospital bought enough song books for every child on the wards. Bought in large quantities, these cost but ten cents each; so it was possible for every child who wanted one for his own to buy one, the money forming a continuous fund for the purchase of more books. The children's use of the song books and their response to informal singing was gratifying. Six boys in the heart ward asked to have the song books brought to them, so the leader left books with them while she went to sing with the children in the adjoining room. Those singing by themselves ranged from nine to twelve years in age. They sang for three-fourths of an hour, then asked if they might keep the books over night. The night supervisor reported the next morning:

"As I was going through the heart ward, those boys were singing and having the best time. One boy said, 'Gee, this is a swell book. Lots of good songs in it.' I was surprised at the really good stuff they called their favorites."

In another room six boys showed a surprising interest in singing and sang a great variety of songs. Joe knew many old favorites by heart. Frank and Ed bought song books and the group sang alone or with the nurses and play leaders. Frank asked if he might buy another book. "But you have one like this, wouldn't you like a different sort?" he was asked. "No, I want this one for my mother; she loves to sing and she will like this one, it's a fine book." He was much pleased when there was singing in two parts and always finished with the invitation, "Come and harmonize with us again." One boy said, "Let's see if 'Home Sweet Home' is in here; there was a peanut man sang that. I asked him to sing it over and over and he did and I cried. I went over to the car and cried, he sang it so swell."

The children in the orthopedic ward greatly enjoyed sing-ing. One boy newly re-admitted said at once, "Let's sing! We used to have fun singing when I was here before." Singing sometimes changed the behavior of patients that were considered "problem children." A girl of eleven was sent in by the psychiatric clinic. When admitted she was a decidedly grouchy child whose feelings were easily hurt. She used her deformed hand to frighten other children and seemed to enjoy being disagreeable. The boys and girls in the ward were singing when she was first admitted; she was given a song book and permitted to make her choices like the rest. She wanted to sing long after the others were through and bought a book after her first experience in sing-ing. She had a good voice and she showed improved per-sonality traits every time she sang. After her more gracious attitudes were revealed during her stay in the hospital, her mother promised she might take singing lessons.

MUSICAL INSTRUMENTS. Volunteers skilled in playing soft toned instruments, such as the flute, zither-harp, or ac-cordion, came to the hospital once a week over a period of three years and accompanied the children's singing. In addition to singing, the children individually and in small groups experimented in playing harmonicas, jews'-harps, toy pianos, xylophones, and rhythm band instruments.

RHYTHM BAND. The children of all ages enjoyed an ele-mentary form of rhythm band used either by itself or as an accompaniment to singing games and songs. Infants from eighteen months to two years seemed happy to be a part of the group as they shook their bells or cymbal sticks. Rhythm play may be expressed with any available sticks. Leather-thonged sticks from jumping-top sets that had been donated but that could not be used by children in beds, made excellent rhythm sticks and the thongs were useful in suspending the metal triangles.

The first band was composed by an odd lot of toy instruments, such as xylophones, tambourines, bells, and a broken drum. From time to time other instruments were added, such as triangles, cymbals, klit-klats, and jingle sticks.

Whenever rhythm-band instruments were presented to a new group in the ward, it was essential that they should not become merely noise makers. Starting with the rhythm sticks alone was found to be a good plan. To keep from any suggestion of formal conducting, familiar games such as "Did You Ever See a Lassie," "Adam's Sons," "Farmer in the Dell," and the like, were used. The children, while keeping good rhythm with their sticks, beat time in whatever ways appealed to them. During the chorus or refrain the child who was "It" often changed the manner of beating time, such as holding his sticks above his head, behind his back, or even under his upraised leg, the others being required to follow suit.

The same principle worked when using instruments—triangles, drums, cymbals, tambourines, and bells. In "Farmer in the Dell," for instance, only one child, who was the farmer, played an instrument during the first verse. When the farmer chose his wife, the two played their instruments or beat their sticks, and so on, players being added in succession as the game itself demanded. The games and songs made for orderly playing and kept the play from being merely a disturbing or distressing element to ill children in nearby rooms, yet they all had the fun and musical experience that might otherwise have been denied them if each child had been permitted to play without this organization by means of a game or song. The children showed much ingenuity in suggesting well-known songs and singing games that could be acted out while playing with sticks and instruments.

LISTENING TO MUSIC. A fine old Swiss music box with about two dozen classic records was greatly enjoyed by the children. Its gay, tinkly music appealed even to the infants, while older children were interested not only in the music, but also in this mechanical device for making music. Victrolas were used on certain floors and every ward had its radio.

In some of the current studies undertaken by parents and educators throughout the United States, those who work with children may find many helpful suggestions on the effects on the children of radio programs.

DRAMATIC PLAY. Additional opportunities for discovering latent abilities, for inducing the expression of a variety of interests, and for developing new skills were given in the form of play by means of arts and crafts. They spent many hours acting out scenes based on home, hospital, and city life, airports, stores, circus, and filling stations. They loved to dramatize stories, songs, and nursery rhymes. Even when lying flat in bed they compensated for their inability to move about by vividly imagining they were doing so. One group of girls in the heart ward made up the plot and the girls acted out their own Christmas play. Other children made and colored their own puppets and gave little plays with them.

DRAWING AND PAINTING. The children enjoyed finger painting, which was first demonstrated with the children and the nurses on the convalescent ward by its originator, Ruth Faison Shaw. Thereafter, it was used successfully on most of the wards. The administrators and nurses were won over when they found that the paints were harmless even if swallowed, and that they wash out easily from clothing and sheets. The children needed no inducements to experiment, but dabbled contentedly covering large sheets of paper[16] with the designs which their arms and fingers produced in the colors. Some of the doctors appreciated the freedom in body movement which this form of play produced and recommended its use particularly with the crippled, spastic, and heart patients.

Boxes of water colors, crayolas, crayons, and pencils, large sheets of bogus paper, newsprint, and cardboard were available for the children's use in expressing their imagination, and their color sense. Obviously, no models were placed before them. In drawing, painting, free hand paper cutting, and clay and wax modeling, the children used the materials freely and with an easy confidence that produced original work. Rather than having the materials constantly at hand it was found best to bring some of it to the children as they needed it, thereby making an appeal by its freshness. The children responded then with vigor and enthusiasm.

CONSTRUCTION AND CRAFTS. In addition to the art materials, the children had blocks of many sizes, shapes, and colors, and construction sets of wood and steel pieces, such as Tinker Toys, Meccano, Erector, or Stanlo. Knitting their own caps, scarves, and bedroom slippers or weaving on hand looms proved attractive to both boys and girls. Crocheting and work in needlepoint were successfully done by some of the girls from nine to thirteen years of age. Both boys and girls enjoyed simple wood work, brass, and wood tapping, and making some of their own games.

16. Pieces of oilcloth large enough for the children to experiment with freely may be substituted for paper and used over and over.

In construction and crafts emphasis was placed on the value to the child in discovering his own powers along several lines rather than on making a nicely finished product. The children under twelve years of age seemed more interested in experimenting with what they were able to do with the materials at hand than in producing carefully finished products such as adults admire. Ethically, it seems better that the child make his own product as best he can, and not have an adult do part of the work for him.

ODDS AND ENDS USED AS PLAY MATERIALS. Every hospital has many unutilized resources that may be drawn upon for play materials. Kitchens, laboratories, sewing rooms, carpentry and repair shops, and storerooms all have waste materials valuable for use in play. Cardboard from cartons make firm boards upon which pasting, coloring, drawing, and painting may be done and are especially suitable for children compelled to lie on their backs. The X-Ray laboratories furnish various sizes of black paper appropriate for cut-outs. Empty boxes can be transformed into games, doll furniture, and toys, and can also be used in the orderly organization of game cabinets and shelves.

The carpenter's shop has odds and ends of wood for simple wood work. Two-by-fours are easily converted into building blocks; and by nailing the covers on empty cheese boxes, hollow blocks, light and easily handled, can be made. Fruit crates may be made into furniture for playing store and house, and their thick partitions make serviceable weaving boards. Empty bandage tubes are useful as sets of tenpins and may also be used with blocks in the children's building. Wooden thermometer holders, too, are an addition to building materials.

Experience has shown that such odds and ends are conducive to imaginative play and develop creative ability to a far greater degree than do such finished commercial equipment as cardboard houses, airplanes and the like that require only assembling.

Commercially made nests of well-constructed wooden boxes usually cost from one to two or more dollars a set, and when the less expensive, easily broken types are given to infants in the hospital, they are often found in pieces on the floor. A serviceable substitute may be supplied by the kitchens. Nests of tin cans from a half pint to quart size are available in such quantities that each child might be supplied with a set. The new methods of opening cans produce a smooth, even edge that cannot injure even an infant's tender hands. Other advantages of using cans lie in the fact that they are easily sterilized and that they cannot be pushed through the bars of the beds. Older children frequently use them with blocks in building, and also in imitative play.

Discarded articles from the kitchens, such as lard pails, egg-beaters, large spoons and boxes, are more substantial, and therefore better for the children's play in the sand and in playing house and store, than are the fragile articles for such play that are sold in toy departments. Discarded broom and mop sticks painted and cut into proper lengths make large size pegs for peg-boards, or they may be used for dowel sticks in wood work. The dowels sometimes used in wooden coat hangers can be made to serve as rhythm- or drum-sticks.

RESOURCES OUTSIDE THE HOSPITAL. Local stores often send to the hospital empty boxes, samples of cloth, paper dolls from discarded fashion books, spools of many sizes, wall paper sample-books, shop-worn books, toys, games, cast-off decorations, and the like. Ribbons salvaged from floral bouquets and used for hair ribbons by the girls had an unfailing psychological effect upon them. They revealed their delight when permitted to make their own selections. They brightened visibly and appeared to rise in their self-esteem when wearing these colorful ribbons for Sundays, special events, or dramatic play.

These odds and ends are not merely a substitute for commercially made playthings but serve to stimulate inventiveness in the children. Whereas commercially made playthings are for the most part complete and offer no incentive for inventiveness, odds and ends are valuable only when used inventively.

In contradistinction to the method usually employed in occupational or physio-therapies, all these activities are presented as play and according to the children's desires, not as class or individual work projects, nor as aids in the cure of some specific disease. There was a decided difference in the results when the handicapped child participated in an occupation because it was play, full of interest and fun for all and not merely a specific remedy prescribed for a physiotherapy treatment, because each child's attention was directed away from his disability toward an objective intriguing in itself. Released from the inhibiting effects of focusing their attention on their disabilities, the children made free, spontaneous responses. Their creative abilities were stimulated and their interest was sustained.

In health, the body and the mind function smoothly as a harmonious, integrated unit; in illness, processes become antagonistic to each other. The various therapies can better overcome this antagonism when they deal with the child as a whole.

This separating of the physical from the social aspects of the child appears to limit the effectiveness of any treatment. The study of the disease biases the study of the child. When physical exercises are prescribed for the individual child, he goes through them in a bored, half-hearted fashion, usually under constant prodding and compulsion. His is the attitude of the child kept after school to make up work. Where the group play method is used, inhibitions are released and the child responds unreservedly, wholeheartedly, and spontaneously, to the stimulation of group interaction. This indirect method, that summons the total organism to action because of the situational appeal to the whole person, indicates amazing possibilities for removing blockages.[17]

As one specialist in play put it:

"Experience has shown that the very nature of the arts and play activities are conducive to the free functioning of the whole person, conducive to unstudied, released activity.... In other words, the expressive aspects of human nature flow more freely through the arts and play than through work."[18]

What is meant by the whole personality can best be shown by the following quotation:

"In using the term 'whole' as applied to a person, who is, of course, almost always changing, that person must be considered as a 'whole' not in the sense of his being complete, but of his being an ever-changing unit. This is no mere catch phrase. It is improbable that any of us treats others as social wholes: yet there are trends in that direction as well as in the opposite. If, however, in dealing with human beings, we are trying to free ourselves from false premises and to think critically of the whole individual in relation to the whole situation—remote as well as immediate—we are sure to grow in the ability to sense and act

17. Schlotter, B. and M. Svendsen, "Experiment in Recreation with the Mentally Deficient," obtainable from the State School at Lincoln, Illinois, and from The Institute of Juvenile Research, 907 South Lincoln St., Chicago, Illinois.

in relation to more of the whole than if our intelligence is blocked by stereotypes based on segments of personality or rigid conceptions of situations." [18]

Special Activities

PARTIES AND OUTDOOR PLAY. By making use of two roofed porches, a covered pavilion and a large campus, play in the sunshine and fresh air was provided for orthopedic and convalescent children. The pavilion was used as an open air school in which play, nature study and academic work [19] were carried on when weather conditions permitted. Birdhouses, gardens and trees added to the attractiveness of the campus.

Puppet shows, chalk talks, parties, and other special events took place there, also. The lawn was so ample as to make unnecessary close contacts between patients of the different wards. Children who could not come out regularly were sometimes brought for special entertainments, such as dog and pony shows, vaudeville performances, and certain holiday celebrations.

Active play, according to their needs, was provided for the crippled and convalescent children in the form of croquet, battledore and shuttlecock, ball and bowling games, and a modified form of miniature golf. A limited amount of apparatus was provided—a low slide, swings of varied types, low teeters, seesaws, wagons, scooters, and tricycles, the latter being the most popular. Swings were second in popularity. There were five sand boxes, with suitable equipment, toys,

18. Boyd, Neva L., "Social Group Work: A Definition with a Methodological Note," Vol. 1, p. 5, Northwestern University Division of Social Work (April, 1937).
19. The Chicago Board of Education supplied four grade school teachers for the children in the hospital, and the Sunbeam League supplied a kindergarten teacher, all of whom worked in hearty coöperation with the Play Department.

and large blocks that were used for constructing train systems, airports, and service stations, and other forms of imaginative play. A playhouse in which the children could stand erect was a source of joy to them in playing house, store, and tea parties and for similar activities. They washed and decorated the walls, and made furniture from orange crates, supplemented by simple furnishings large enough for their own use in playing out various forms of social life familiar to them.

PARTIES AND ENTERTAINMENTS. The monotony of long months in a hospital was broken by parties, by celebrations of the various holidays, and by an occasional entertainment. The value of any special event was estimated by the director of play according to the degree of participation it afforded the children. Parties were often no more than the well-loved games, songs, and stories together with refreshments and decorations. Served in the middle of the afternoon, ice cream in itself always made a party in the eyes of the children. A free choice of hair ribbons from floral bouquets (often sent in quantities to the hospital) made the girls feel "all dressed up" for a party. Paper caps always served to make both boys and girls feel festive.

All children who were not too young or too ill had a share in the plans for parties and holidays. They designed their own valentines and Christmas and Mothers' Day greeting cards. From empty egg shells salvaged from the diet kitchens, the older children made character dolls or place cards for Easter, and all who were old enough to hold a spoon dyed Easter eggs. These activities were carried on by children confined to their beds as well as by the few who were able to sit about a table. From the older convalescent and orthopedic children who were up and about, the children often selected a small committee to go to the recreation office and select the games and play equipment for the special parties on the wards.

Hallowe'en was always a favorite holiday. Even crippled children who were compelled to lie flat on their backs or in other positions while confined in heavy casts or braces designed and made out of paper bags, masks that completely covered their heads. If the children suspected that an adult was coming into the ward, on would go the masks to "fool" him. The head nurse entered into the fun by changing the name tags on the beds and then moving the beds around to "fool" the doctors and nurses during the period of the party.

As a convenience in carrying on the games and stunts at the party, the children on the orthopedic ward were grouped for the afternoon according to chronological ages.

Board members and other friends often provided special parties and entertainment that, months afterward, were happily recalled in detail by the children. Easter with its procession of bunnies, spring flowers, and lollipops; Christmas, preceded by letters to Santa, by the crèche, and by many groups of carolers singing on the campus or in the corridors and ending with Santa himself distributing gifts, were joyously recalled in detail. For a special holiday, friends of the hospital often sent in boxes of fresh stationery, cards, and valentines from which the children selected greetings for their friends.

On the three largest wards, a favorite entertainment was a chalk talk given annually. The children selected the themes and took turns drawing the initial lines for the artist, who turned them into fascinating pictures and related them to the theme originally selected by the children. Months later the children were found with crayolas, pencils, or paint, busily working out "chalk talks" on bits of paper, even using the paper towelling when the supply of more suitable paper was not at hand.

Nurses and doctors kept careful check on what children were permitted to have parties. Children not too ill were given the fun of anticipation and of making preparations in advance of the eventful occasion. Cardiac children were rarely told in advance, because the doctors thought it was over-exciting for them.

FAVORS. Favors, such as adults seem to consider necessary for a party, received but the momentary interest accorded any novelty. With the exception of paper caps and hair ribbons, which seemed to aid in producing a gay, "party-like" feeling, favors added nothing to the children's enjoyment, and, in fact, seemed to inject wholly unnecessary sophistication into a children's situation. As mementoes of a party, the children seemed to prefer keeping the special paper napkins or plates on which the ice cream, candies, or cookies had been served.

PRIZES AND REWARDS. As has been said before, no prizes, awards, nor other devices for emphasizing individual excellence were ever used in the hospital.

NATURE STUDY. For years an outside private organization provided teachers for nature study in the hospital. These teachers came every Saturday morning throughout the year, and usually three mornings each week in the summer. They carried on discussions about birds, butterflies, flowers, and stars, supplemented by pictures, lantern slides, and star maps. Special effort was made to follow up any newly awakened interest; bird, flower, and animal games were in daily use; pets, such as canaries, guppies, goldfish, and small turtles, were brought into the hospital. The children planted flower and vegetable seeds. Very proud of their achievements were the convalescent boys when they turned prune containers into neatly sandpapered and painted flower boxes. They selected their own seeds, planted a combination of vegetables and flowers and later enjoyed eating sandwiches made with the lettuce, carrots and radishes they raised.

THE CHILDREN'S LIBRARY. In May, 1932, there were five hundred books in the Children's Library of the hospital. By November, 1937, the number had increased to 4,068. Gifts from friends provided the major portion of this collection. All were accessioned, catalogued, and organized according to library methods. A branch of the Chicago Public Library provided a librarian to distribute books two days each week.

Not counted among the 4,068 books were hundreds of inexpensive ones that artists and writers have produced during the "depression." These were used for displays for nurses and other groups outside the hospital, and for distribution among the children on the wards. Their low cost made it possible to buy them for children too young to be given the more expensive volumes and for those whose illnesses kept them out of school so long that they needed the elementary knowledge in pleasing form to encourage them to read.

Six magazines suitable for children—*Activities, Child Life, Junior Red Cross, National Geographic, Nature Magazine,* and *Story Parade* were in circulation, as was *The Weekly Reader*—a news sheet printed especially for children.

Only books of fine quality were given to the children. In many instances the powerful influence of children's books and radio programs was shown, especially by the patients admitted to the fracture ward. There were those who frankly stated that they had been imitating Tarzan, and others whose restless nights and disturbed dreams were traceable to reading overstimulating and exaggerated stories.

The most vivid example of such reading was that of a nine-year-old boy who stayed in the hospital for a short time because of a fractured bone. He was surprised that the nurses did not recognize him at once. "Don't you know me? Why, my picture was in all the papers. I'm the boy that gave the detective story to the boy that killed the little girl in the icehouse. I read all about what to do in the books." He was asked, "Where do you get your books?" "Oh, there's a man at our corner that has a rental stand, for one cent each," was the reply. "Don't you ever go to the public library?" asked the nurse. "Oh, I went there once, but they didn't have any interesting or exciting stories like the rental stand. I like the kind that makes the pimples (goose flesh) come out." After consulting with the play director regarding the library resources, the nurse was given Kipling's *Rikki Tikki Tavi,* which she read to him. He was so interested that he snatched the book from her hand; she could not read it fast enough for his eager interest. Other good literature that opened new vistas for him followed. Of *Emil and the Detectives* he said, "Say, I could hardly wait to see how the story came out." The social worker was given these facts about the boy so that she might help him in his reading upon his release from the hospital.

Another boy who had read little before coming to the hospital developed such an enjoyment of reading during his long illness in the hospital that he read every book he could get from the Children's Library there. When dismissed, he went to the branch library to get a reader's card and to thank the librarian in person for acquainting him with so many fine books.

The fact that sick children are more sensitive than well children is claimed by many authorities. In contrast to everyday events—varied experiences and contacts with normal persons that tend to counteract or weaken the force of unwholesome impressions for the well and physically active child—the environment of the sick and convalescent abounds in restrictions and monotony that tend to intensify and fix impressions. Illness itself tends to deepen such impressions. Particular care was taken, therefore, in selecting books.

During the long days of convalescence, or the months and years of care for the chronically ill, those in charge of them have a rare opportunity to offer their patients fine literature. The injection of "psychic germs" into the impressionable minds of children by their reading of trashy, gruesome, overstimulating tales is probably more subtle, dangerous, and far-reaching than the physical germs and bacteria about which there is so much concern.

Exercising care in selection does not mean the elimination of virile literature and the substitution of spineless, "goody-goody," sentimental types. Neither does it mean replacement of all fairy and fanciful tales with the so-called "factual" stories, but rather the elimination of all gruesome, unwholesome and overstimulating tales. In the hospital, the physical make-up as well as the content of a book was considered. Many books are so heavy as to be a strain upon the sick child's strength, while the type in others is so small as to cause eye strain. Such books were rejected. In evaluating books for children, Agatha Shea, Director of Children's Work for the Chicago Public Library, set up the following criteria:

Undesirable Features in Books for Children

1. Over-stimulating adventure and exaggerated situations
2. Reformation or instruction of adults through activities of child characters

3. Impossible accomplishments on the part of children, in a realistic story

4. Unethical situations in home, school, or among playmates

5. Inaccuracy in factual books

6. Poor format, highly glazed or spongy paper, small print, etc.

A worthwhile book is marked by

1. Child, not adult situations

2. Characters that are true to life

3. Wholesome ideals

4. Plausible adventures

5. Subject of interest and value to children

6. Authenticity of factual material

7. Well written text, appropriate vocabulary, etc.

8. Good format, large clear print, good paper, attractive illustrations

In recent years a number of books written at the child's level will help to lessen his fears of doctors, dentists, and hospitals. Vera S. Flandorf, Librarian, Children's Memorial Hospital, Chicago, compiled a list of more than a hundred arranged by grades from one to twelve and by subject. Some help before admission to a hospital, others are interesting during convalescence. She has graciously permitted its recommendation and a sampling here. A few examples are:

			Grades
Beim, Jerrold. *Danny and the dog doctor.*	Morrow, 1950	2-4
Danny mends a robin's broken wing.			
Dudley, Nancy. *Linda Goes to the Hospital.*	Coward, 1953	K-5
Preparation for an operation.			
Elting, Mary. *First Book of Nursing.*	Watts, 1951	4-6
Gives accurate information in an interesting way.			

Other types tell of famous doctors and nurses or of children and animals overcoming difficulties. Her list, *Books to Help Children Adjust to a Hospital Situation,* and other pamphlets on play may be obtained from National Society for Crippled Children and Adults, 2023 W. Ogden Avenue, Chicago 12, Illinois.

Caring for the Sick Child at Home by Marion Lowndes, published in 1955, covers every phase of care, possible activities, and sources of help. Nearly all recent books on child care and development devote a chapter or more to the convalescent child (see Bibliography). The Health Education Service of the John Hancock Mutual Life Insurance Company, Boston, Massachusetts, has two helpful pamphlets: "Caring for the Sick in the Home" and "Diversions for the Sick." These are free and may be obtained on request to the Company or from your local Health Department.

SOURCES

Alpha Omega Chi, Chamber of Commerce Bldg., Indianapolis 4, Ind.
  Toy Book.
  Self-Help Toys to Make for Handicapped Children. Free.
American Heart Association, 44 East 23rd St., New York 10, N. Y.
  Have Fun—Get Well.
Association of Childhood Education International, 1210 15th St. N.
W., Washington, D.C.
  Children's Books.
  Work and Play Catalog.
Children's Bureau, U.S. Government Printing Office, Washington, D.C.
  Your Child from One to Six $.15.
  Your Child from Six to Twelve $.20.
Child Study Association, 132 24th St., New York 24, N. Y.
  Books of the Year $.25.
Institute of Child Development and Welfare, University of Minnesota,
Minneapolis 14, Minn.
  A few samples at ten cents each. (Send 8 cents postage on return
  envelope if two or more are ordered.)

Books for Young Children.

Music for Growing Children.

Finger Plays for Young Children.

Play Equipment for Young Children.

Metropolitan Life Insurance Co., New York 10, N. Y. has free pamphlets:

6-8, Years of Discovery.

Understanding Your Young Child.

National Recreation Association, 8 West 8th St., New York 11, N. Y., has material on every phase of play and recreation.

Recreation Standards for Children's Institutions $.15.

Starting a Recreation Program in a Civilian Hospital, Beatrice H. Hill, $1.00 (1952).

The Uses of Recreation in a General Hospital, B. H. Hill and E. M. Cohen.

National Society for Crippled Children and Adults, 2023 West Ogden St., Chicago 12, Ill.

Your Child's Play $.25.

Many others. Send for lists.

Science Research Associates, Inc., 57 W. Grand Ave., Chicago 10, Ill.

Emotional Problems of Illness, Irene M. Josselyn, M.D.

CHAPTER 5

PLAY IN CLINICS FOR CHILDREN

What challenge faces those in charge of children's clinics today? Is physical care their only concern? What efforts are made to bring past methods in line with facts learned in many fields of research on the child and his needs? How can clinics help the total development of children now that research has proved the physical, emotional, social, and ethical aspects are interwoven and cannot be treated separately? Is there value in teaching parents, nurses, and volunteers by actual demonstrations of activities? How can a play specialist help? Has play other uses in a clinic than keeping children quiet or entertained?

The Challenge

The health program of doctors and nurses is well organized, functions well, and needs no comment. The challenge comes in trying to fit a complete health program to "the child's world" nature's way for him to grow and to learn, and therefore better fitted to meet his needs and interests than adult ideas or convenience. Intensive research the past fifty years in many lines reveals this need *whenever* a child is dealt with. Planning without considering the possibilities in play in which a child thinks, acts, and reveals himself spontaneously because of play's appeal to the total personality limits both the adults and the child. True play offers mutual advantages. It serves many more purposes than keeping a child quiet or entertained. It can, and should be, a highly valuable integrative experience. Deep and abiding impressions are made on a child's mind, feelings, and attitudes in the early years. To quote Faegre, Anderson, and Harris, authors of *Child Care and Training,* on preparing the child for painful experiences:

"Trips to the doctor's or dentist's office are sometimes painful or frightening or both. Although emphasis on good child care has greatly improved the modern doctor's understanding and handling of children, there are some situations when pain simply can't be avoided, or when abrupt handling of a child just does occur."

"Young children show fear of any sudden, unexpected happening, particularly if it is quite new to them or they do not understand it. Furthermore, children seem to react more intensely than adults to physical pain and very quickly develop strong fears of persons or places associated with painful experiences. Even the infant not infrequently cries on the occasion of his second or third shot at the sight of the doctor's white coat or needle."

Administrators of hospitals and clinics, increasingly aware of and concerned with the total development of patients, provide a play specialist for work with children. Happy experiences too have lasting effects and can lessen the shock of painful impressions. Experience over a number of years shows that children recall vividly the game played in a hospital even in a short stay. Months later, sometimes years later, they described in happy recollection every detail of the games played. This was true of the well child who came for minor operations as well as of those who were in for longer periods. It IS important that every agency dealing with children consider the child's viewpoint and provide constructive types of play.

How Can a "Play Lady" Help?

The clinic situation presents a number of conditions that call for imagination, initiative, and quick adaptation to meet various needs. Where developmental levels show a wide range, activities provided must hold the attention of the children but not be exciting or exhausting. They can be divided into groups with equipment and games that appeal so each player can derive benefits according to his ability. Chronological age is not a reliable guide. Play must be fun, truly social, and offer some new creative experience.

When guided by a specialist who understands children in various developmental stages and who knows the values and uses of many types of activities, play can be very effective in clinics. It can be a real help to the child, to his parents, to doctors, nurses, and volunteers. The child acts wholeheartedly with spontaneous enthusiasm, and cooperates better because he and his parents are at ease. It makes the waiting easier, happier, and more interesting, and lessens the strain on all present. Adults, especially young parents, see play methods new to them. Older ones may recall some similar activity they enjoyed in childhood. Adults often take part in clinic play and so realize better the attraction, the skill required, and the child's joy in accomplishment in what may seem to the parent a very simple game.

Adult Education

Interesting leaflets on child care are usually at hand on bulletin tables for conferences and for adults to take home. But children cannot read these. They learn best by action, by using the entire body in play. In clinic play parents see how they respond to guidance that does not dictate but stimulates interest.

Because of inadequate understanding of John Dewey, who advocated more progressive methods than the dictator ways of an earlier period, young parents have been filled with belief that "the child knows best" and should have complete freedom. They are confused and ineffective sometimes in dealing with children. Some read every book possible. One very conscientious mother said: "My child doesn't do a single thing the books say he should do at this age. Should I take him to a psychiatrist?" Some parents are so busy they "don't have time to play or read books."

Observations of several children from various backgrounds playing wholeheartedly reveals more than can be obtained by reading books, however good. Parents see their child or children at a new angle. The child is not static but more like a color organ, revealing new aspects of his personality in each new situation or group.

A Young Child Looks at the Clinic

"My! What a *big* room. It's bigger than any at our house. What a nice place to run and jump." He does so, but someone soon stops that, so he starts to climb a chair. "These are big chairs, for grownups, but children are in them. Some are wiggling and turning. They don't like to stay there." His climb isn't easy for those are folding chairs and just as he thinks he is about to reach the top of this "hill," his glow of possibly accomplishing this feat of mountain climbing is shattered. The ledges of the "hill" fold up. His body, hands. and fingers are caught and held in a sudden crushing grip from which he has to be rescued and calmed down.

Soon he sees boxes in a corner. "Those kids seem to have blocks and toys. I'll go see." This time he seats himself on the floor as a safer place. "Ugh! this floor is cold. It's a lot colder than when I stand or someone holds me up." He forgets the cold as he examines the contents of the boxes and plays with them. He sees a boy and a girl arrive. "They're sure in a hurry about something. Wonder what they're after." Curiosity drives him. He discovers they've been here before and are urging a lady to let them play a game they had the last time they were here.

Since he is a "Big Boy," all of three years old, he watches the game intently and joins in the fun. If the first is a table game, he is pleased to see the chairs are his size. "They just better be! I don't want to be hurt again by a mean old chair. That scares me, and it's most uncomfortable. I just couldn't get loose by myself." But he soon forgets his past fright as he becomes absorbed in the game.

After that a different kind of game is played. Whether an action game, rhythm, a finger play, or folk game, it has been carefully selected by the "Play Lady" because of its appeal to a wide range of ages. It sometimes is a good experience for older and younger children to play together. In the last two games parents played with them. "Why, they seem to be having as much fun as we are." Now it is his turn to be weighed. He leaves the group knowing he can come back for more play until the doctor wants him. When that time comes he isn't a frightened child, tired out with long waiting. He has been living in his world of play that he enjoys and understands so he has had time to forget his earlier frustrations. Fun with folks he had never met gave him new social experience. Why can't adults arrange the situation so a child can be spared unfavorable aspects as far as possible? The kinds and placement of furniture provide only one example.

THE PLACE. The place where clinics are held varies greatly

since a clinic may be in a settlement house, a school, a Veteran's Post, a regular health center, or a hospital. Often the place is not equipped for play. Storage space is usually limited, though the children may have a table or a shelf with books, and choose toys from a box for individual use. The play space is often small and limited to a corner of the room. The children may not run about to get rid of excess energy while waiting for what seems to them an interminable time, and for a purpose they may not understand and may even fear.

PEOPLE PRESENT. In addition to the doctor or doctors, the nurses conferring with parents and arranging future visits, the volunteers and aides keeping routine methods running smoothly, there may be visitors from college classes or agencies studying procedures. Always there are the children accompanied by one or both parents, an aunt, or grandparent. Sometimes, in addition to those having appointments, sisters and brothers are brought along who could not be left alone at home, so there may be four or five children present in one family. Ages range from tiny babes in arms to those five or six years old, or include all ages through high school. Usually, all except infants are seated in rows on chairs built for adults as they wait their turns to be called.

Values in Simple Equipment
and
How Used in Clinics

At home, adults are often disappointed to see children uninterested in or destructive of expensive toys and games. Most children are interested and develop initiative in using their imaginations when playing with materials and parts of equipment adults throw away. Boxes, cartons, cans, bottle tops, pieces of wood and cloth—all these in various sizes have fascinating uses in their play.

A few of the different types of activities that were favorites, copied for use at home and welcomed in return visits to the clinic "where we go to play" are given here as examples. They use simple materials, require little space, are easily cleaned, and readily discarded when necessary. They can be made as service projects by the aged, by youth groups, and by the children.

A toy that keeps baby interested is an empty coffee can with clothespins along the rim—either the regular or the spring type—that he can grasp, pull off, return to the rim, or that make a lovely noise when he drops them. If too noisy, the can may be padded.

Investigating mother's handbag is always an attraction, sometimes to her annoyance. Using an old handbag or partially covered box, a considerable age range can have fun. Small objects are in the bag: a toy, ball, bell, necklace, pencil, eraser plastic spoon, etc. with more complicated items for older players. A lone child keeps busy examining each object. Older ones place them in orderly fashion for their idea of a store or house, or play a game they call *That Feeling Game* or *Mrs. Santa*. The leader starts it by saying: "Mrs. Santa has some different and funny things to give you in this bag. Hold your hands behind your back and she'll put something in them. Don't look. Just feel and see if you can tell what it is." Repeat with different objects at each turn. Use with one child or with a *small* group, so each gets to feel before being tempted to look.

BEAN BAG CATCH. This is popular, first with throws back and forth between a leader and each child in turn, then as a

Surprise because no one knows to whom it will be thrown. This adds to the fun after they have shown skill at catching and throwing in the first version. Bean bags are better than balls for clinic play. They need not be large for younger children and can be kept clean by covering the cloth with plastic. This is easily wiped off if dropped on muddied floors.

BLOCKS. Blocks of various sizes and shapes always appeal, especially when spools, boxes, tubes etc., are added. Green-vegetable trays tied together make good flatboats to carry objects in imaginative play. Odds and ends of scrap lumber add variety to constructive inventions in creative play with blocks or as a game.

DON'T LET IT TOPPLE. These scraps may be used in a building game. Heaped in the center of a table and drawn one at a time—or each player may draw five or six at the start—the object is for each child to place his bit of wood so carefully on the one previously put there that the growing structure does not topple over. The varied sizes and shapes are a real challenge. There is no penalty if the structure falls. Players start over to see if it can be kept up longer. (Rough edges should be sandpapered before use, a project for a service group looking for something different from making scrap-books. Bean bag boards with triangles of different sizes on larger scrap are good projects.)

Adapting Old Favorites

Target games appeal to many. For younger children the appeal is stronger and more lasting when their vivid imagination enters into the play instead of scoring by numbers. They love to pretend. As they express it: "Let's play pretend."

CHASE THE PIGS INTO THE BARN. For this a front view of a barn with an open door has been drawn and cut from cardboard, and side views of three separate pigs. Ears, eyes, tail and legs must be sketched on each side of a pig or some literal-minded three-year-old will say: "I don't want to play with that pig. He isn't all there." Each child in turn has three pigs to throw through the barn door one at a time. It sounds easy but requires judgment and skill. Many an adult fails the first time and soon realizes the child's pride when he succeeds in getting all three pigs into the barn. Throwing distance is increased as skill is gained. Older children and mothers often copy these pigs for use at home.

PRETEND PARTY. Mark nine or twelve sections on the back of a large calendar or window shade and in each paste a colored picture of a good food: an orange, milk, ice cream, sandwiches, hamburgers, etc., cut from magazines. At the top or center section paste a picture of a boy and girl supposedly giving the party. A small bean bag, rubber ring, or plastic bottle top serves for throwing. The finished article is placed on a low table or floor.

Children enter readily into the fun as you say: "Here's a boy and a girl who've invited you to a party. You can have anything you want to eat. Tell us what you want before each throw." Each has a turn. This is repeated until they have as many foods as they wish. If a throw overlaps two sections both foods are his.

Variations: *Toys I Like, A Trip to the Farm, To The Zoo,* or miscellaneous objects may be used. Those scientifically minded could take *A Trip to the Moon.* Older children like the sections marked with numbers so they can count scores as they play alone, or with others in teams or as individuals.

The usual table, board, or floor games such as *Carroms,*

Bull Board, Croquet, Shuffleboard, and the like can be adapted by drawing the designs on cardboard or plywood in reduced sizes. *Carroms* becomes *Circle Target,* using plates of different sizes in drawing circles and numbering each circle. From one to four players can have fun using checkers to snap into the circles. Checkers in piles of two or three can indicate arches for a game of *Croquet* with two taller piles as stakes. Each player has a different color for his snapper as they play according to the usual rules.

Favorite Card-matching Games

For many years *Bird Lotto* and *Take the Pack* have been the joy of hospitalized children, as well as of those who are well. Packets of fifteen bird cards in color may be purchased at ten cents each from Church and Dwight Company, 10 Cedar Street, New York City. Each player has a sheet of colored construction paper nine inches by twelve inches on which five or six birds are pasted. The object of the game is to match all those birds from duplicates drawn from the center of the table or from a box top. Players draw in turn from these face-down cards, holding up his drawn card for all to see. The one who first says: "Mine" because it matches one of his places it face down over its duplicate on the larger card. The first to match all his birds is winner. This doesn't stop the game for there are second, third, or more winners since merely winning is not as important as matching all the cards.

Several good picture lotto games played the same way are sold in stores, i.e., *Animal Lotto, Object Lotto, Things That Go,* etc. The commercial *Bird Lotto* with nine birds on each card is liked by older children.

TAKE THE PACK. Deal one card to each player and one face up in the center of the table. Repeat four times. The child at the left of the dealer tries to match a bird from his hand with one in the center. If successful, he starts his pile in front of him for all to see; if not he discards a bird to the center. Since the object of the game is to get as many birds as possible, each one tries to capture some other player's pile by matching with one from his hand rather than matching a single card in the center. When the first hand of four is all used, a second hand is dealt to each but not to the center if four or more cards are left there. Too many cards are difficult to watch when several are playing.

Play Without Material Equipment

Volunteers, aides, and parents are often at a loss without equipment. They are more familiar with active playground games, relays, team games, and individual sports. Knowledge of play possibilities without equipment meets many needs and is especially important in hospitals, clinics, homes, or where space is limited. The social types of play are useful in meeting special needs, problems of behavior, or social development. Here the play specialist has a valuable contribution. Play is of the spirit and is not dependent upon material equipment. Types can be taught that give parents, nurses, teachers, and social workers more confidence in dealing with children because they promote better relationships.

Magic and Mystery Games

So-called magic games fit well into a clinic situation. They use the senses of hearing, seeing, feeling. Some are a challenge to adults as well as to children over nine. Interest continues regardless of interruptions by new arrivals or others being summoned. They intrigue the restless by appeal to curiosity. Even young children enjoy "reading minds."

MIND READING. "Can you read minds?" the leader asks. "Surely you can if you can count to ten." Quickly they prove it by counting beyond ten. "When you are "IT" just place your hands on the cheeks of the one who chooses a number—like this—and if everyone thinks hard of that number you will feel it." "IT" blinds his eyes while another holds up a number of fingers for all to see. "IT" then feels the cheeks of the chooser and of a few others, including the leader, and promptly gives the correct number to the amazement of all, including his parents. CLUE: The leader showed "IT" how it is done by clinching his jaws a few times without moving his lips in the first demonstration of how to place the hands. Usually the child is so pleased he does not become a "Wise Guy" and tell how he knows, but he helps the leader in the next rounds so others have fun through their own experience, when it is their turn to try.

BLACK MAGIC. Someone chooses an object in view while "IT" has his eyes shut. A leader calls "IT" back and points to different objects saying: "Is it this?" a few times. "IT" answers correctly for he was told beforehand to watch for something black because the next object pointed to is the right one. When the leader merely points, without saying anything, it seems even more mysterious.

MAGIC THREE. The group decides on one of three similar objects: three doors, pictures, or windows in plain view, while "IT" blinds his eyes or withdraws. The leader then calls "Come in. Tell us which was chosen." "IT" answers correctly because the leader's *first* word gave the clue, the signals being "Come" for No. 1, "All right," for No. 2, and "Ready" for No. 3 as the first word in any sentence by the leader, the objects always numbered from left to right. All who get the idea become "IT" and demonstrate their ability.

A silent version uses the sense of sight. The leader and one other know the signal will be some movement to the left, right, or middle. If No. 1, the leader puts his hand on his left hip or points the left foot.

Once they know how it is done, adults are likely to see no reason in continuing a magic game. Not so the children. They play these over and over even when everyone has the answer. WARNING: In any magic game, NEVER switch from one set of signals in the middle of a game without warning. It frustrates the players; it isn't fair play; it spoils the fun and kills the very spirit of play, making players resentful of any leader who does so. Start the play by saying there are some games that call for careful listening or watching; would they like to try one? If the game involves hearing, say: "Listen carefully a few times, and you can be "IT" when you get the idea." Let them get the experience of solving the mystery.

Many adults refuse to play games because of some past frustration in play or fear of being made objects of laughter or derision in some stunt. DO NOT USE TOO MANY OF ONE TYPE in one session. Magic games call for close attention. Too many at one time tire the players.

Old favorites that continue to appeal are so numerous that only a few can be given here as examples:

A.B.C. OR ALPHABET. Two or more players take turns naming

objects in view beginning with a letter of the alphabet. The first might say "Arm," the next "Arch," etc. according to the number of players. Any letter may be chosen. For younger children objects are used instead of letters. One says: "I see something red." Others take turns guessing what was chosen.

BIRDS FLY. A leader calls: "Birds fly. Ducks fly, Horses fly," while waving his arms for "flying." Players must wave their arms only for those that fly. When a mistake is made, that child becomes leader.

TWO LITTLE DICKEY BIRDS. This finger game is especially intriguing if the leader has two tiny scraps of gummed paper pasted just below the nails of his index fingers to represent birds. These are held forward, the others closed into the palms as the children all recite:

> Two little dickey birds sat on a hill,
> One named Jack, the other named Jill.
>   (Move Jack forward, then Jill.)
> Fly away Jack! Fly away Jill!
>   (The left and then the right finger is folded under a thumb
>   and quickly replaced by the middle fingers.)
> Come back Jack! Come back Jill!
>   (Reverse for Come Back.)

Knowing finger and action play, short stories and story play, riddles, tricks, nonsense games, and songs equips a nurse, parent, or play leader with no materials to meet the needs of a variety of ages and situations. *Ball for Baby* and *Piggie Wig* from Emilie Poulssen's *Finger Plays* are much liked. The children chant and play along with the leader. They enjoy repeating them.

Rhythms, Action Songs, and Singing Games

Children respond readily to rhythm in total body action. Where a playroom is part of the clinic, there are hundreds of songs and singing games from all over the world to suit every mood. If not, it is possible for children to enjoy rhythm play without disturbing adults, by chanting softly instead of singing the words of some familiar song or game. An empty oatmeal box, serving as a drum, may be tapped with fingers for others to guess the tune after the player states the type, i.e., nursery, patriotic, cowboy. Rhythm sticks cut from thin dowels, each twelve inches long, can be used alone or with the drum in follow-the-leader in whatever fashion he holds and beats his instrument.

Chanting is easy with any song that has a decided beat. Players walk in a circle around a child in the center for the first two lines, then stop and repeat whatever action the center child chooses, during the next two lines. Examples: *Did You Ever See a Lassie? Adam's Sons, While Traveling Over Sea and Land,* and *Miss Sue.*

MISS SUE

> There's *some*/one in my *cell*/ar, Miss *Sue*/, Miss *Sue*/,
> There's *some*/one in my *cell*/ar, Miss *Sue*/ from *Al*/a *bam*/.
> Did you *ev*/er see a *monk*/ey make a *mo*/tion, Miss *Sue*/,
> Miss *Sue*/?
> Did you *ev*/er see a *monk*/ey make a *mo*/tion, Miss *Sue*/from
> *Al*/a *bam*/?

THIS OLD MAN. Appeals to a variety of ages, with the different actions of this the Old Man stroking his beard each time he is mentioned. The first verse is given in full, the others in outline. Each verse ends with the refrain.

> This Old Man, he played *one,* (Hold up pointer finger)
> He played knick knack on his *thumb.* (Tap left thumb with right fist.)

REFRAIN: Knick knack, paddy whack, *throw* the dog a bone.
(Tap and throw.)
This Old Man came *rolling* home. (Winding motion of
both hands.)

VERSE   2..........he played *two*..............on his *shoe* . . . etc.
3........................... *three*...............*knee* . . .
4........................... *four*...............*floor* . . .
5........................... *five*...............*hive* (Chase bees) . . .
6........................... *six*...............*sticks* (Tap left finger
tips.)
7........................... *seven,*...............He went flying up to
Heaven . . .
8........................... *eight,* ....He played knick
knack on his *pate* (head).
9........................... *nine*...............*spine* . . .
10........................... *ten*...............He went rolling once
again . . .

Since waiting for the doctor's examination may take an
hour or more, it is not necessary nor wise to have games fill
the entire time. What is needed is an atmosphere lacking
tensions or strain. Even tiny babes are remarkably sensitive to nonverbal communications, to strain, or to a calm
"social climate." Babes in arms are their mother's responsibility. The toddlers and preschoolers are the actively restless ones. A few minutes may seem hours, an hour like a
day. This appointment may interfere with the usual nap. He
may be timid or aggressive or afraid of others because he is
an only child.

Adults watchful of each child, his interests and responses, will learn many things. The child's humor and ways of
thinking and acting are all different from adult ways. Adult
patterns just do not fit for they have little meaning for a
child, but even a babe responds to play.

When toys are wisely selected, toddlers are happy with assorted blocks, small pull wagons, rubber dolls, animals, simple wooden trains, trucks, autos, telephones, etc. Usually they are very imaginative and should be allowed to use toys as they choose as long as they do not hurt each other or interfere with clinic needs. If a child shows interest in what the next older ones are doing, he plays with them as long as his attention lasts. Perhaps he sees mothers and older children playing paper-and-pencil games, so he wants to try. He will scribble happily by himself on large sheets of newspaper, newsprint, or cardboard, and proudly display his handiwork. Adults who seek to correct his effort or show him how to use his toys are the ones responsible for his outburst of irritation, anger, or crying.

CHAPTER 6

SUGGESTIONS FOR GIFTS OF PLAY
EQUIPMENT FOR CHILDREN
IN A HOSPITAL

Organizations, such as men's and women's clubs, lodges, churches, Sunday schools and other youth organizations, as well as individual persons, often asked for suggestions regarding gifts for the children in the hospital. A report on the experiences at The Children's Memorial Hospital may prove helpful to organizations that have philanthropic service as a part of their programs, and to individuals with specific children in mind. Before making a donation, then, it is advisable to consult with the superintendent of a hospital because no two hospitals present identical conditions, even though children's play interests are similar and serve as guides in the selection of playthings. Experience has shown that certain types of playthings are especially acceptable to the children and a genuine help to the staff. For example, for a number of years a professional group of women helped to build up the children's library by gifts of carefully selected books each Christmas time. Various donors contributed to a library of song books. This collection, confined to songs particularly suited to children's voices, served not only for the children's use, but for the teaching of songs to nurses, volunteer workers and parents to be used with children. A quantity of inexpensive collections of songs sent to the children by one generous friend made it possible to provide every child with a book during periods of singing.

One Christmas, children in two grades of a public school selected ten-cent story and picture books instead of making scrapbooks for the children in the hospital. They chose those with clear print and pictures, omitting all books with overstimulating plots and impossible situations. Such books place too great a burden upon children whose imaginations are overtaxed already by illness. When one's head is dizzy with imagined patterns on walls, and when even the furniture takes on strange forms, one is in no condition to read overstimulating tales and the malaise of illness and convalescence makes gruesome tales unsuitable.

Experience proved that donated scrapbooks were likely to be too bulky for sick children to hold, and their contents of but momentary interest. Lightweight blank scrapbooks, however, of approximately eight by eleven inches in size, made of firm paper, are a better substitute. Such books have found favor among the children, who enjoy filling in pictures of their own choosing. Sent together with used stamps from many countries, empty stamp books stimulated a stamp hobby that all the boys in one ward carried on for months.

Gifts that permitted the children themselves to do something, that stimulated their creative abilities, provided for more continued interest than most ready-made play equipment. Handicraft tools, rarely found in sufficient quantities for all the children even in one ward, were acceptable gifts. Sets of large blocks, sand boxes, a large playhouse often absorbed a group of children for hours in playing house, store and hospital. Solidly built furniture of sizes to accommodate the children as well as their dolls, and in a variety of colors, were much enjoyed. The so-called "unbreakable" dishes made from colorful plastic materials in various styles and sizes appealed to the children.

Rhythm band instruments, such as triangles, rhythm sticks, bells on leather strips, klit klats and drums afforded much enjoyment. A simplified drum is now obtainable, made of a flat board with material stretched over a circle at one end to form the drum section. Soft toned musical instruments such as harmonicas, recorders, shepherd's pipes, ukuleles, ocarinas and the like afford many hours of enjoyment.

A large box of yarns in assorted colors, together with bone knitting and crochet needles, kept the children busy and interested for months. Both boys and girls learned to crochet caps, bed slippers, bags, pillow tops, purses, table runners, afghans, colonial mats, and scarves that could be worn on the sun porches in cold weather. Pieces of brightly colored, small-patterned percale, large enough for dolls' clothes were also hailed with delight by the girls.

The children used over and over again gifts of clay for modeling. Each child had as a minimum half-pound boxes of permoplast and plasticine, oil clays in soft colors that do not come off on hands or clothing. Modeling wax, too, was used.

Such things as scissors with good cutting edges and blunt ends and library paste for each child are acceptable gifts, since but few hospitals can afford to give to each of its hundreds of children even one of these simple things.

Many kinds of small automobiles and airplanes stimulate hours of imaginative play for boys. Purchasers should make sure that these are light in weight and have no sharp points projecting at wheel centers and that toys that have removable rubber tires or other small parts go to the older children, not to those small enough to swallow them. The new, light, streamline models made of hard rubber, with their wheels covered and all unnecessary projections removed, are most suitable for a hospital.

Unbreakable toys are best for children in hospital wards because they have very little space in which to keep their possessions and, as their beds are high, great damage is done to any breakable plaything that falls. For younger children, toys and blocks should be large enough to prevent their slipping through the bars in the sides of the beds, light enough to be easily lifted, and strong enough to stand much banging about. Soft, stuffed toys and furry animals are unsuitable in a hospital because it is too difficult to keep them clean. Guns, soldiers, glass encased or covered puzzles, jig-saw puzzles with hundreds of parts, heavy books or those with fine print, and large toys are not suitable for children confined to their beds. In selecting books for infants it is advisable to confine them to the washable cloth type.

Baby dolls with unbreakable heads and washable bodies proved to be greater favorites than any other type, especially when outfitted with simple layettes taped or buttoned so the children could easily dress and undress them. Rubber dolls were liked by the younger children who seemed satisfied with large squares of cloth to dress them with, rather than complete clothing.

For boys and girls from nine to twelve or thirteen years of age the Make-It-Books offered many suggestions for using odds and ends for handwork. Since these booklets may be bought for ten cents, one might be given each child on the ward. The mediocre color and cut-out books so prevalent and so often selected for children are poor gifts. They give the child very little to do creatively, and are so crowded with objects that they leave him nervous and harassed in trying to complete them. Booklets of the punch-out type are also objectionable. Far superior to this commercial "busy-work" are plain pads of paper with crayolas or pencils, or finger paints, that are far more useful than the usual color or paint books with figures already outlined.

Many of the ready-to-assemble type of plaything, such as model airplanes or boats, require the energy and perseverance of a normal adolescent or adult to put them together and are therefore unsuitable for sick or convalescent children.

The children in this hospital have been best satisfied when all in the ward received identical gifts; for example, as simple a thing as a fresh box of crayolas for each child, jumbo size for the little children and the smaller size for the older ones, or pads of plain paper that can be used for drawing and painting, paper cutting, or paper folding, gave the children great pleasure.

Since the diet of sick children must be carefully planned, gifts of candy, fruit, or other food are not acceptable to a hospital if intended to be given directly to the children. In any case the hospital superintendent should be consulted before making any such purchases.

As a matter of convenience play materials are here listed on age-levels. These age divisions should be regarded as merely rough classifications and the lists of play materials as suggestive. Although the children of widely different ages played with the same materials, they used them quite differently.

Play Materials for Children

AGES 6 MONTHS TO 3 YEARS

Aluminum cups, dishes and pans

Animals (rubber)

Balls (rubber)

Books (cloth or heavy cardboard)

Blocks
Clothespins
Dolls (rubber)
Nests of boxes, cans, and dishes
Paper and large crayolas
Peg boards with large pegs
Pieces of bright cloth
Playkies
Pyramids (wooden rings, squares, triangles, etc.)
Spools and strings of spools
Spoons
Wooden trains, autos (simply constructed)

AGES 3 TO 6 YEARS

Animals (rubber or wood)
Beads (large)
Blocks (building and design)
Clothespins and cloth for dresses
Cloth for dolls' dresses
Dishes (aluminum, tin, and safety ware)
Dolls (rubber, with clothes that button)
Doll furniture
Laundry, housekeeping and store equipment
Musical toys
Paper (large sheets)
Paints (finger and water color)
Plasticine or permaplast
Peg-boards, various types
Picture books—brief stories
Puzzles (Jig-saw or wood and on few pieces)
Scissors (blunt, with sharp cutting edges)
Soapbubble pipes
Transportation toys
Wall paper sample books
Wax (modeling)

AGES 6-8 YEARS

Blocks (building and design)
Books of short stories (illustrated and light in weight)
Cloth (scraps large enough for doll clothes, tablecloths, etc.)
Dolls (washable and unbreakable)
Dishes (tea and cooking sets)
Equipment for playing airport, circus, farm, home, store, etc.
Feltograms and papergrams
Paints (finger and water color)
Paper (plain, colored, wallpaper, crayolas and soft pencils)
Paste
Puppets (hand)
Puzzles (fairly simple ones)
Scissors (blunt)
Spool knitting
Wax (modeling)
Weaving looms

AGES 8-12 YEARS

Blocks (building and design)
Clay
Construction devices (Erector, Meccano, Stanlo, Tinker Toy, etc.)
Construction materials (paper and odds and ends)
Dolls and doll furniture
Dishes (tea and cooking sets)
Equipment for circus, farm, home, airport, store, etc.
Feltograms and papergrams
Materials for hobby interests
Painting and drawing equipment
Parquetry and mosaics
Plasticine or permaplast
Puppets
Puzzles
Sewing materials
Scissors
Wax (modeling)
Weaving looms
Wood and tools
Yarn, bone crochet hooks and beading needles

Special Equipment for Convalescent and Orthopedic Children Not Confined to Their Beds

Doll carriages
Kiddy Kars
Push and pull toys
Sand box equipment
Tables and chairs (low)
Tricycles and pushmobiles
Wagons

The play materials listed here are general classifications of types usually available. New playthings are offered each year in bewildering quantity and varied in quality. Some are products of research on children's interests. A recent guide for selecting is *The Complete Book of Children's Play* by Ruth E. Hartley and Robert M. Goldenson. It not only classifies children's responses from babe through adolescence, but grades books, toys, songs, music, nature, crafts. magazines, and sources of help. Not as detailed is *The Child and His Play* by Hazel Kepler. Both are based mainly on the well child. In choosing any equipment the interests of the particular child must be kept in mind and the realization that a sick child often regresses to a lower level. *Caring for the Sick Child at Home* by Marion Lowndes is practical. Many recent books on child care listed in the Bibliography have a chapter on the sick child.

Experiments with various types of toys have been tried in hospitals. Grace Langdon, Ph.D., Child Development Advisor to the American Toy Institute in New York City, has written leaflets: "A Study of the Uses of Toys in a Hospital," and "How to Choose Toys for Convalescent Children." These and others are available free from the National Society for Crippled Children and Adults, Inc., 2023 West Ogden, Chicago 12, Illinois.

Well-selected toys serve as one phase of constructive care. Even the tiny babe in a hospital or in his own home senses a lack if adults rely on play equipment alone. More than material things, his instinct demands recognition as a human being, which even a few minutes of play with others can satisfy. The social element of cooperation satisfies him emotionally.

Some of the new arts and crafts equipment make acceptable gifts and are easy for a child to use. Brushes are not needed for painting or pasting because tubes of paint or paste are held like a ball-point pen directly on the material. Another type of paint like a large crayon needs only to be dipped into a little water. New materials similiar to plastilene can be used over and over. Paper and plastic compositions even have gummed backs so no paste is needed. All these can be found in crafts shops and general variety stores. The Kleicar Corporation, Chelsea, Michigan has a lightweight plastic peg-board called Rub-R-Art on which a child can make designs by stretching rubber bands from peg to peg. Design blocks of firm plastic and pull-a-part beads of different sizes, shapes, and colors are available.

For music, a fine gift to a hospital's play department is an autoharp and playing instructions. This soft-toned instrument is easy to carry for singing accompaniments and soothing restless patients. The method for playing is easily learned. Many nurses, volunteers, and children learn quickly. New song books that are useful with it are: *Autoharp Accompaniments to Old Favorite Songs* by Elizabeth Blair, published by Summy-Birchard, Evanston, Illinois, 1958; *How to Play the Autoharp, Including 31 Favorite Songs,* by Frances Hall, Boston Music Co., 1956; *Harmony Fun with the Autoharp,* by Beatrice Perham Krone, Neil G. Kjos Music Co., Park Ridge, Illinois, 1952.

How to Play the Recorder is a self-instructor for use as melody or descant by Arthur Harvey, Sam Fox Publisher, New York, 1960. *Enjoy Your Recorder* by the Trapp Family Singers, 1954, can be obtained from Distributors Inc., Sharon, Conn.

New Standard Harmonica Course by Margaret J. Symberg, 200 songs with words, 1954, and 5 *Minute Harmonica Course Self-Teaching Method,* 1953, are both published by M. N. Cole, Chicago, Illinois. *Fifty Famous Songs for the Harmonica,* 1954, is published by Robbins Music Corporation, N. Y.

To meet the growing demand for knowledge of other nations the Cooperative Recreation Service, Inc. Delaware, Ohio, has a number of new booklets such as: *African Songs,* 1958; 15 *Austrian Songs,* 1959; *A Sampler of Japanese Songs,* 1958; *Merry Songs* (Hungarian), 1957, and so on. Others are collections from various countries in a single booklet, as in *Sing Together Children,* 1959, and *Songs for All Time,* 1946, as well as booklets on games, riddles, dramatic stunts etc. Published "for use and not for profit" these are usually twenty-five or thirty cents a copy, and less in quantity rates.

Schmitt, Hall & McCreary Co., Minneapolis, Minnesota have: *Songs Children Sing,* arranged by Florence Martin and Margaret Rose White, 1943, and *Sing with Action* by Rita Kiltz and Hazel Neff, 1958.

CHAPTER 7

CLASSIFICATIONS OF TESTED FORMS
OF PLAY

Since play is an emotional attitude, something determined
by the mind or spirit rather than by the physical activity involved, children not acutely ill can enjoy many forms of
genuine play even when the nature of the illness makes
physical inactivity mandatory. A wide range of play is possible to meet their developmental needs without in any way
conflicting with the necessary restrictions, or fatiguing the
patients. On the contrary, experience has shown that certain
play activities aid in fostering attitudes of happiness, harmony and coöperation, in promoting emotional balance, and
in integrating the total personality. Experience has demonstrated that such activities may be the means of releasing
emotional tensions and of stimulating the participants re-
freshingly.

For the benefit of those responsible for children's welfare,
lists of tested play activities are given. Many of these have
proved effective not only for children under thirteen years
of age (the age limit treated in this book), but in hospital
work with adolescents and adults, and in institutions for the
mentally disturbed.

Many persons who attempt to play with convalescent
children feel quite at a loss, particularly when confronted by
the many hospital situations in which the patients must be

kept in bed, often flat on their backs, or in restraints; those in which no material equipment is permitted to be passed from one child to another; and where there is a wide variance in the ages of the children. For their convenience, play activities have been classified to indicate those requiring no material equipment, as well as those which require equipment. For the convenience of those parents or nurses who must play with the individual patient in the home or in the hospital, certain games possible for two persons to play are indicated. References are to standard sources. However, since the children themselves made up their own variants, and since the nurses and volunteer workers used games familiar to themselves, the source of every game listed could not be given.

Some games which require a certain amount of physical activity such as dancing, skipping in a circle, tagging, and the like, may often be adapted to patients in bed by omitting these elements. The appeal of the traditional games, even in the mutilated forms resulting from such adaptation, was a never-ending source of amazement to the play leaders. The children's imaginations fill in these activities which braces, casts, or other confining apparatus prevent their bodies from executing. They appear happy, in spite of these handicaps, in playing the kinds of games that normally active children enjoy.

The social quality of most of the games listed will be found helpful in overcoming the sense of psychic isolation which hospital regulations tend to magnify, particularly on the part of those children who are on precaution, isolated, or separated in cubicles, burn tents, or restraints. Playing in small groups appears to be far more effective for the social, emotional, and ethical development of the hospitalized child beyond nursery age than the individual play so often used.

Types of Play for Patients in a Hospital and Suitable for Those in Bed

PLAY ACTIVITIES REQUIRING NO MATERIAL EQUIPMENT

1. Dramatizing everyday scenes, short stories, poems, nursery rhymes, and songs
2. Learning nonsense rhymes, poems, and counting-out rhymes

> Aldis, Dorothy, *All Together,* New York, Putnam, 1952.
>
> Brooks, Leslie, *Johnny Crow's Garden,* New York, Warne, 1958.
>
> De la Mare, Walter, *Peacock Pie,* New York Holt, 1957.
>
> Cole, William, *Humorous Poetry for Children,* Yonkers, New York, World, 1955.
>
> Lear, Edward, *Complete Nonsense Book,* New York, Dodd, Mead, 1956
>
> Morrison, Lillian, *A Dillar a Dollar,* New York, Crowell, 1955.
>
> Opie, Iona and Peter, *Oxford Nursery Rhyme Book,* New York, Oxford, 1955.
>
> _____, *Lore and Language of School Children,* New York, Oxford, 1960.
>
> Salaff, Alice, *Words Are Funny,* Garden City, Doubleday, 1952.
>
> Whithers, Carl, *A Rocket in My Pocket,* New York, Holt, 1948.
>
> _____, *Counting Out,* New York, Oxford, 1946.

3. Finger plays

> Jacobs, Frances E., *Finger Plays and Action Songs,* Lothrop, Lee, and Shepard, 1941.
>
> Pierson, J., and R. Wood, *Wonder Book of Finger Plays and Action Rhymes,* New York, Wonder, 1955.
>
> Poulsson, Emilie, *Finger Plays,* New York, Lothrop, Lee and Shepard, 1939.
>
> Salisburg, Helen W., *Finger Fun,* Los Angeles, Coroman, 1955.
>
> Sumner, Florence, *Let's Play with Fingers,* Chicago, Whitman, 1948.

4. Enunciation tongue twisters
5. Folk and singing games (see list, p. 155)
6. Other types of games: sense, intellectual, and those requiring control of impulses
7. Telling stories
8. Rhythm play (described in Chapter 4)
9. Riddles, puzzles, jokes, tricks (see p. 161)
10. Sign Language

   Hofsinde, Robert, *Indian Sign Language,* New York, William F. Morrow & Co., Inc., 1956.

   Tompkins, William, *Indian Sign Language,* San Diego, Wm. Tompkins, 1927.

   Wallace, F., and E. Kirby, *Your Symbol Book,* New York, Campfire Girls, 1951.

11. Singing

Activities for Two or More Persons Requiring No Material Equipment

GAMES

All these games are more fun when played in groups, and are particularly useful for children on precaution. Games that may be played by two persons are indicated by (c) Numbers indicate the books where descriptions of the games may be found. See list, p. 154.

c A.B.C. 2, 4
Adverb, In the manner of 5, 7, 8, 14
Air, Fire, Water 6, 7, 8, 11, 14
Alibi 14
Animal 2
Animal or Dumb Spelling 7, 9
Aunt Tessie 8
Auto Game 8, 10

Backward Spelling 11
Barnyard Din 5
c Beast, Bird, Fish 2, 4, 7, 9
Big Round Full Moon 8, 12, 14
Birds or Ducks Fly 5, 7, 8, 11, 13
Black magic 1, 2, 6, 10, 12, 13
c Buzz 1, 4, 5, 6, 12, 14
Chain Spelling 6, 8

Numbers refer to the following books:

1. Bancroft, Jessie E., *Games* (rev. ed.), New York, Macmillan, 1937.

2. Boyd, Neva L., *Handbook of Games,* Chicago, FitzSimons, 1945.

3. ————, *Hospital and Bedside Games,* Chicago, FitzSimons, 1945.

4. ————, *Schoolroom Games,* Chicago, FitzSimons, 1945.

5. Eisenberg, H., and L. Eisenberg, *Family Pleasure Chest,* Nashville, Parthenon, 1951.

6. ————, *The Omnibus of Fun,* New York, Association, 1949.

7. Forbush, W. B., and H. R. Allen, *Book of Games for Home, School and Playground* (rev. ed.), Philadelphia, Winston, 1954.

8 Gardner, Ella, *Handbook for Recreation Leaders,* Washington, U.S. Government Printing Office, 1936.

9. Harbin, E. C., *Fun Encyclopedia of Games,* Nashville, Abingdon, 1940.

10. Kraus, Richard, *Play Activities for Boys and Girls,* New York, McGraw-Hill, 1957.

11. Leeming, Joseph, *The Real Book of Games,* Garden City, Country Life Press, 1953.

12. Mason, B. S., and E. D. Mitchell, *Social Games for Recreation,* New York, Barnes, 1935

13. Rohrbough, Lynn, *Handy Kits,* Delaware, O., Cooperative Recreation Service, n. d.

14. Wackerbarth, M., and L. Graham, *Games for All Ages and How to Use Them,* Minneapolis, Denison, 1958.

PLAY ACTIVITIES REQUIRING MATERIAL EQUIPMENT

1. Working puzzles, and practicing sleight of hand feats (string tricks, etc.)
2. Anagram games (see list p. 159)
3. Card games (see list p. 159)
4 Games of skill
5. Pencil and paper games (see list p. 160)
6. Modeling with clay, paper, pulp, wax, etc.
7. Codes: International, Morse, etc.
8. Construction with blocks and other building devices
9. Drawing and designing
10. Painting with fingers and with brushes
11. Making puppets and giving puppet plays
12. Sewing
13. Needlepoint
14. Crocheting
15. Knitting on spools or with needles
16. Weaving
17. Rhythmic play with sticks, balls, etc.
18. Playing musical instruments
19. Nature study
20. Paper cutting and tearing
21. Paper dolls
22. Table and board games (see list p. 163)
23. Tricks
24. Woodwork

FOLK AND SINGING GAMES

By omitting actions such as walking, skipping, or dancing, many of these are adaptable to bed patients. They may be used as songs or for dramatizations. For children waiting for operations or in some clinics and playrooms, they may be used entire. Sources are indicated by number.

Adam's Sons 3

Bingo 5, 8

Needles Eye 3, 5, 6

Oats and Beans 1, 2, 5, 6

Cats and Rat 3
Clap and Trap 3
Clap Dance 4
Did You Ever See a Lassie? 1, 2, 5
Dog and Hare 3
Dollar, Dollar 2, 5, 7
Farmer in the Dell 1, 5, 6
Green Gravel 5, 6, 8
Here Comes a Bluebird 5, 8
I Am a Musician 3
I Sent a Letter 5, 6
Jenny Jones 5, 6, 7
Kings' Castle 3
Lead Soldiers 3
London Bridge 1, 5, 6
Miss Sue
Muffin Man 1, 4, 5
Mulberry Bush 1, 5, 6

Old Roger 5
On the Bridge of Avignon 1, 6, 7
Our Shoes Are Made of Leather 5
Poor Mary Sits A-Weeping 5
Princess Thorn Rosa 4
Ring a Ring o' Roses 5
Roman Soldiers 1, 5, 6
Round and Round the Village 6
Saw and Saw the Lumber 2, 3
Skip to My Lou 8
This Old Man 2
Walk in the Moonlight 3
When I Was a Young Girl 5
While Traveling Over Sea 3
Will You Know 3

Numbers refer to the following books:

1. Bancroft, Jessie E., *Games* (rev. ed.), New York, Macmillan, 1937.
2. Bley, Edgar, *Best Singing Games,* New York, Sterling, 1957.
3. Boyd, Neva L., and Dagna Peterson, *Folk Games and Gymnastic Play,* Chicago, FitzSimons, 1932.
4. ———, *Folk Games of Denmark and Sweden,* Chicago, FitzSimons, 1932.
5. Boyd, Neva L., and Florence W. Brown, *Old English and American Games,* Chicago, FitzSimons, 1932.
6. Forbush, Wm. B., and H. Allen, *A Book of Games for Home, School and Gymnasium,* Philadelphia, Winston, 1954.
7. Harbin, E. O., *Fun Encyclopedia,* Nashville, Abingdon, 1940.
8. Rohrbough, Lynn, *Handy Play Party Book,* Delaware, O., Co-operative Recreation Service, n. d.

GAMES FROM MATERIAL AT HAND

From materials readily found in any hospital or home

many games may be made. The asterisk indicates which ones may be made. The letter c indicates games that may be played by two persons. The numbers refer to books containing descriptions for playing.

*c Anagrams (see list p.159) 3, 4, 7, 12, 13
   Animal 2
*c Bean Bag Games 2, 3, 7, 10
 c Bounce Ball in Box 2, 6, 9, 10
 c Bowls (adapted) 2, 10
   Button Button 2, 7, 10, 11, 13
   Card Games (see list p.159)
   Cats and Dogs (I have a Dog) 2, 6, 13
   Change Places (Observation) 7, 9, 10, 13
   Consequences 5, 9, 12
   Fishing, Fishing 2
*c Fish Pond
   Fool Teacher 2
   Hands Up 1, 2
 c Hide in Plain Sight 7
 c Hide the Clock 2, 8
   Hold Fast, Let Go 7, 10
 c Hide the Thimble 1, 2, 7
 c Hull Gull 2, 5, 6, 9, 11
   I Received These Scissors 9
   I Spy 2, 5, 6, 9, 11
   Jackstones 1, 3, 9

   Jingle Keys 2
* Lotto Games
*c Lummi Sticks 12
   Match Tricks 3, 10, 12 (use toothpicks)
   Mrs. Santa (Feeling Game) 2
   Observation 5, 7, 9, 10, 13
   Odds or Evens 5, 7, 9, 10
   Pencil and Paper Games (see list p. 160)
   Poison 2, 7, 9
 c Rhythm Play 2, 6, 10
*c Ring a Peg 9
   Ring on a String 2, 7, 9
*c Ring Toss 9
   Roll Over Come Back 2
   Table and Board Games (see list p. 163)
*c Target Flip 2, 3
*c Target Throws
   Teacher, or Go Last 2, 4, 7 (adapted)
   Tenpins 2
   Up Jenkins 1, 2, 5, 7, 9, 11

Numbers refer to the following books:

1. Bancroft, Jessie E., *Games* (rev. ed.), New York, Macmillan, 1937.
2. Boyd, Neva L., *Handbook of Games,* Chicago, FitzSimons, 1945.
3. ———, *Hospital and Bedside Games,* Chicago, FitzSimons, 1945.

4. _____, *Schoolroom Games*, Chicago, FitzSimons, 1945.
5. Eisenberg, H., and L. Eisenberg, *Family Pleasure Chest*, Nashville, Parthenon, 1951.
6. Forbush, Wm. B. and H. R. Allen, *A Book of Games for Home, School and Playground*, Philadelphia, Winston, 1954.
7. Harbin, E. O., *Fun Encyclopedia*, Nashville, Abingdon, 1940.
8. Mason, B., and E. D. Mitchell, *Social Games for Recreation*, New York, Barnes, 1935.
9. Rohrbough, Lynn, *Handy Kits*, Delaware, O., Cooperative Recreation Service, n. d.

Game equipment such as checkerboards and anagrams, commonly found in most institutions and homes, may be used in a number of ways. For example, these may be played on a checkerboard:

1. Straight Checkers
2. Give Away
3. Five in a Row (Go-Ban) Kit N
4. Fox and Geese
   From their end of the board the four Geese move forward only, and diagonally. The Fox, who always has first move in the game, moves forward or backward on his black squares in an attempt to break through a gap in the Geese's lines as they advance and try to surround him.
5. Helma (like Chinese Checkers)
   Played with six checkers each in opposite corners by two or four players. If only two play, ten checkers for each may be used if a longer game is desired.
6. Reversi or Friends, 3 and Kit N
7. Streamline
   Played like Chinese checkers except that players may jump over an entire line of checkers, in any direction, but may not remain in any other person's corner space.

In wards where children are not allowed to touch another's game or equipment, players may still have the fun of playing together by numbering squares alike on two boards. Each plays alone on his board equipped with both colors of checkers and moves the ones representing his opponent's men to correspond with his opponent's moves.

ANAGRAM GAMES

Anagrams, Game of Words, Lettergrams, Lexicon, are names used by commercial firms selling cardboard, wood, or card letters. Directions for various games come with them. They may be played by those over nine or ten years of age.

Adjectives
Anagrams (three letters exposed)
Clock Solitaire (in Lexicon)
Dictionary
Fifteen Letters (make three-letter words)
Lexicon

Logomachy
Stealing Words
Store
Tangled Words
Words and Sentences from letter sounds
Word Solitaire (in Game of Words)

CARD GAMES

African or Chinese Rummy
Animal Whist
Authors
Bird Lotto
c Camelot
c Canfield
c Casion
c Concentration
c Fan Tan (Seven Up)
Flinch
Four Seasons (Solitaire)
Game of Words
Go Fishing

c Octagon
Old Maid
Peter Coddles
Pyramid
Pig or Donkey
Pit
c Queen's Audience (Solitaire)
c Quick Wit
c Rook
Round the Clock (Solitaire)
c Russian Bank
Sixty Six
Slam Bang

Hearts	c Snatch (or War)
c I Doubt It	Sorry
c Kan-U-Go	Spoof
c Lexicon	Take or Steal the Pack
Michigan	Tuxedo
Muggins	War

These games are more fun when several persons play together. The letter c indicates which may be played by two persons. Hoyle, the standard source on card games, has been compiled by several editors. Recent editions for card games are:

Moorehead, A. and G. Mott Smith, *Hoyle's Rules for Games,* New York, New American Library, 1958.
————, *Complete Book of Solitaire,* New York, Longmans, Green, 1949.
Quinn, Vernon, 50 *Card Games for Children,* Cincinnati, U. S. Playing Card Co., 1949.
Sheinwold, Alfred, 101 *Best Card Games for Children,* New York, Sterling, 1956.

PENCIL AND PAPER GAMES

Many of these may also be played using a blackboard where all may see. The letter (c) indicates games that may be played by two persons. Numbers refer to books with descriptions for playing.

Art Consequences 5	c Hang a Man 3, 5, 7
Artists' Relay	c Indian Signs and Symbols
Battleship 5, 8, 9	Logomachy 4, 6
Blind Artists	c London 1
c Categories, Guggenheim or	c Making Boxes or Squares 5, 9,
Vocabulary 3, 5, 7, 11	11
c Codes 11	c Making Triangles 9

Consequences 5

Cootie 5

c Dictionary 3

Drawing Puzzles 3, 10

c Fire Department Got Stuck 3

c Five in a Row
   (Go-Bang) 5, 8, 10

Freak, Crazy, or Composite
   Pictures

c Mixed Names, Nuts, Fruits

c Morse Code

c Naughts and Crosses 3, 6, 9, 11

c Recognition 3

c Train of Thought 9

c Transformation 3

c Vocabulary 3, 5, 7

c Word Making 6

Numbers refer to the following books:

1. Bancroft, Jessie E., *Games* (rev. ed.), New York, Macmillan, 1937.
2. Boyd, Neva L., *Handbook of Games*, Chicago, FitzSimons, 1945.
3. _____, *Hospital and Bedside Games*, Chicago, FitzSimons, 1945.
4. _____, *Schoolroom Games*, Chicago, FitzSimons, 1945.
5. Eisenberg, H., and L. Eisenberg, *Family Pleasure Chest*, Nashville, Parthenon Press, 1951.
6. Forbush, Wm., and H. R. Allen, *Book of Games for Home, School and Playground*, Philadelphia, Winston, 1954.
7. Harbin, E. O., *Fun Encyclopedia of Games*, Nashville, Abingdon, 1940.
8. Mason, B. S., and E. D. Mitchell, *Social Games for Recreation*, New York, Barnes, 1935.
9. Ostrow, O. S., *Pastimes for Two*, New York, Harper and Brothers, 1958.
10. Rohrbough, Lynn, *Handy Kit II*, Delaware, O., Cooperative Recreation Service, n.d.
11. Wallace, Carlton, *Treasury of Games and Puzzles*, New York, Philosophical Library, 1958.

PUZZLES, TRICKS, AND RIDDLES

Sick children get very tired trying to put many pieces of a jigsaw puzzle together. Only older convalescents who are well advanced care for more than fifty pieces, and then prefer to do them in groups of two or three players. Puzzles of three-ply wood that hold together even when at an angle prove more satisfactory than those of cardboard or wood that do not interlock. Puzzles should be carefully adapted to the individual. He should have the satisfaction of completing it himself without fatigue. Puzzles of six or eight pieces, simple in line and color and with objects familiar to them, are much liked by younger children.

For the older children many kinds are suitable if the patient's need and ability are given careful attention. To cite a few examples:

Boole Blocks
Cardboard and Wood Forms
    (circles, squares, triangles,
    etc.)
Checkerboard Puzzles
Crossword
Eleven Blocks
Fifteen Puzzle
Jumbled Words
Jump Two and Only Two
Maze
Metal Ring Twisters

Migration
Nine Blocks
Paper and Feltograms
Puzzle Peg
Pyramid
Reversible Frogs
Shuttle
Star
Tangrams
Thirteen Puzzle
Triangle

Riddles and tricks appeal to many children, particularly to boys. For convalescent children it is better to give but a few at a time because of the mental energy used in solving them. Unlike adults whose interest is often ended when they know the solution, the children like to repeat them over and over. They enjoy trying them out on every new child admitted to the ward and on every nurse and doctor within range. Start them off with one or two and they often recall some they know, or are inspired to make up tricks and riddles of their own.

Many inexpensive collections have been published. This makes it possible for each ward to have its library at little cost, not taking much space because they are usually small books. Here are some for children:

Carlson, G. L., 1001 *Riddles for Children*, New York, Platt & Munk, 1949.

Chrystie, Frances, *Riddle Me This*, New York, Oxford, 1940.

Hoke, Helen, *Jokes, Jokes, Jokes*, New York, Watts, 1954.

Justus May, *Pedlar's Pack*, New York, Holt, 1957.

Leeming, Joseph, *Fun with Puzzles*, Philadelphia, Lippincott, 1946.

_____, *More Fun with Puzzles*, Philadelphia, Lippincott, 1947.

_____, and S. Miller, *Riddles, Riddles, Riddles*, New York, Watts, 1953.

Mellon, Robert C., *Super Duper Riddles*, New York, Hart, 1958.

Morrison, Lillian, *Black Within and Red Without*, New York, Crowell, 1953.

Withers, Carl, and Sula Benet, *American Riddle Book*, New York, Abelard-Schuman, 1954.

_____, *Riddles of Many Lands*, New York, Abelard-Schuman, 1956.

Wallace, Carlton, *The Treasury of Games and Puzzles*, New York, Philosophical Library, 1958.

TABLE AND BOARD GAMES

This list includes both commercial games (indicated by an asterisk), which may be purchased with directions for playing, and games that may be quickly made from materials at hand for temporary use, or more carefully of wood as permanent equipment. Directions for those that may be made are found in the books indicated by numbers. The letter c indicates those that may be played by two persons.

* Admiral Byrd's Little America   *c Kiddidoms
*c Anagram games 3, 4, 5, 6   * Kriss Kross

*c Camelot
  Card games (see list p. 000)
*c Caroms
*c Checkers
*c Chinese or Star Checkers
 c Chinese Friends (Reversi) 3, 7
*c Contack
*c Crokinole
*c Disco
* Doctor Dolittle
*c Dominoes 3
 c Fish Pond
    Rainbow
    Treasure
    Wood
 c Five in a Row
    (Go Ban) 3, 5, 7
 c Fox and Geese 3, 5, 7
 c Fox and Geese
    (on a Checkerboard) 5
    Gomoku 7
    Go-Narabe 7
 c Halma 3, 7
*c Helma 7
* Indian Arrowheads
*c Jackstraws
 c Japanese Corn Game 7
* Junior Scrabble

*c Lotto Games
   Animal
   Bird
   Flower
   Geography
   Number
   Object
   Picture
   Things That Go
 c Match tricks (use toothpicks
   or other sticks) 3, 6
 c Mill 3, 7
 c Nine Men Morris 3, 7
*c Pegity
*c Pick Up Sticks
   Puzzles (see list p. 000)
*c Quick Wit
   Qubic
 c Reversi 3, 7
   Ruma 7
* Shanty
*c Sorry
* Speed
 c Streamline Checkers
   Target games 1, 2, 3, 5
   Tea Party 4
* Tricky Triangles
   Wari 7

Numbers refer to the following books:

1. Bancroft, Jessie E., *Games* (rev. ed.), New York, Macmillan, 1937.
2. Boyd, Neva L., *Handbook of Games,* Chicago, FitzSimons, 1945.
3. ———, *Hospital and Bedside Games,* Chicago, FitzSimons, 1945.
4. ———, *Schoolroom Games,* Chicago, FitzSimons, 1945.
5. Forbush, Wm. B., and H. R. Allen, *Book of Games for Home, School and Playground,* Philadelphia, Winston, 1954.

6. Mason, B. S., and E. D. Mitchell, *Social Games for Recreation,* New York, Barnes, 1935.
7. Rohrbough, Lynn, *Handy Kit,* Delaware, O., Cooperative Recreation Service, n. d.

Activities for the Child Who Must Play Alone

GAMES FOR INDIVIDUAL PLAY

Games ordinarily played by two persons may be used if the player assumes the role of an opponent in rotation.

Anagram games
Balero
Checker puzzles
Diablo
Dramatic play
    airport, circus, house,
    store, stories, etc.
Flags of all nations
Feltograms
Fish pond games
Hand puppets
Jackstraws
Jump two and only two
Lotto games
Match tricks (with sticks
    or toothpicks)
Migration
Nested boxes, dolls, eggs
Nine block puzzle
Nursery toys

Paper dolls
Peg boards
Pick up sticks
Pommawonga
Puzzle peg
Pyramid
Reversi
Shuttle puzzle
Soap bubble blowing (sipping
    straws or spools may be used)
Solitaire card games
Star puzzle
Streetcar game
String tricks
Table golf
Target games
Three-ball tally
Toys
Transformation

CONSTRUCTIVE AND CREATIVE WORK WITH:

Boxcraft
Clay modeling

Mosaics
Drawing and design

Construction devices:
  Blocks
  Erector
  Meccano
  Stanlo
  Stay Built
  Tinker Toys
  (new ones appear each year)
Crochet
Design sets:
  Angle and Curve
  Color cubes

Finger painting
Making puppets
Make up stories, songs, poems
Music and musical instruments
Needlepoint
Paper cutting and tearing
Sewing
Soap carving
Spool knitting
Weaving
Woodwork

BIBLIOGRAPHY

Play and Recreation

Arnold, Arnold, *How to Play with Your Child*. New York, Ballantine Books, Inc., 1955.

Davis, John E., *Play and Mental Health*. New York, A. S. Barnes & Co., Inc., 1938.

Dulles, Foster R., *Americans Learn to Play*. New York, Appleton-Century Crofts, Inc., 1940.

Gulick, Luther H., *A Philosophy of Play*. New York, Charles Scribner's Sons, 1920.

Hartley, Ruth, *et al., Complete Book of Children's Play*. New York, Crowell Co., 1957.

———, *Understanding Children's Play*. New York, Columbia University Press, 1952.

Huizinga, Jan, *Homo Ludens, A Study of the Play Element in Culture*. Boston, Beacon Press, 1955.

Jacks, Lawrence P., *Education Through Recreation*. New York, Harper & Brothers, 1932.

Kepler, Hazel, *The Child and His Play*. New York, Wilfred Funk, Inc., 1952.

Kraus, Richard, *Play Activities for Boys and Girls*. New York, McGraw-Hill Book Co., Inc., 1957.

Lundberg, G., *et al, Leisure*. New York, Columbia University Press, 1934.

Nash, Jay B., *Philosophy of Recreation and Leisure*. St. Louis, C. V. Mosby Co., 1958.

Neumeyer, M. and E., *Leisure and Recreation* (3d ed.). New York, The Ronald Press Co., 1958.

Overstreet, Harry, *A Guide to Civilized Leisure*. New York, W. W. Norton & Co., Inc., 1934.

Pieper, Josef, *Leisure the Basis of Culture*. New York, Pantheon Books, Inc., 1952.

Riggs, Austin F., *Play*. Garden City, Doubleday & Co., Inc., 1935.

Romney, G. Ott, *Off the Job Living*. New York, A. S. Barnes & Co., Inc., 1945.

Slavson, S. B., *Recreation and the Total Personality*. New York, Association Press, 1946.

Soules, George, *Time for Living*. New York, Association Press, 1955.

Varied Activities, Pastimes, and Equipment

Birdsong, June S., *Children's Rainy Day Play*. New York, Laurel Editions, 1953.

Bley, Edgar S., *Have Fun with Your Son*. New York, Sterling Publishing Co., Inc., 1954.

Carlson, Bernice, *Fun for One or Two*. Nashville, Abingdon Press, 1954.

Dow, Emily R., *What Can I Do Now?* Aladdin, 1950.

Eisenberg, H. and L. Eisenberg, *Family Pleasure Chest*. Nashville, Parthenon, 1951.

Fox, L. K., *et al, Children Want to Learn*. New York, Grolier Society, Inc., 1954.

Frankel, L., and G. Frankel, *What to Do with Your Preschooler*. New York, Sterling Publishing Co., Inc., 1954.

Hartley, Ruth, *et al, Complete Book of Children's Play*. New York, Columbia University Press, 1957.

Horwich, F., and R. J. Werrenrath, *Have Fun with Your Child*, Englewood Cliffs, Prentice-Hall, Inc., 1954.

Johnson, June, *Home Play for the Preschool Child*. New York, Harper & Brothers, 1957.

————, 838 *Ways to Amuse a Child*. New York, Harper & Brothers, 1957.

Kaufman, C., and P. Farrell, *If You Live with Little Children*. New York, Putnam, 1957.

Kawin, Ethel, *Wise Choice of Toys*. Chicago, University of Chicago Press, 1938.

Kepler, Hazel, *The Child and His Play*. New York, Funk Wagnalls Co., 1953.

Kraus, Richard, *Play Activities for Boys and Girls*. New York, Mc-Graw-Hill Book Co., Inc., 1957.

Lowndes, Marion, *Caring for the Sick Child at Home*. Philadelphia, Westminster Press, 1955.

McMullin, Marjorie, *How to Help the Shut-in Child*. New York, E. P. Dutton & Co., Inc., 1952.

Parker, Cornelia, *Your Child Can Be Happy in Bed*. New York, Thomas Y. Crowell Co., 1952.

Games

Bancroft, Jessie, *Games*. (rev.). New York, The Macmillan Co., 1937.

Boyd, Neva L., *Handbook of Games*. Chicago, FitzSimons, 1945.

————, *Hospital and Bedside Games*. Chicago, FitzSimons, 1945.

————, *Schoolroom Games*. Chicago, FitzSimons, 1945.

Eisenberg, H., and L. Eisenberg, *Family Pleasure Chest*. Nashville, Parthenon Press, 1951.

————, *Pleasure Chest*. Nashville, Parthenon Press, 1949.

————, *The Omnibus of Fun*. New York, Association Press, 1956.

Forbush, Wm., and H. R. Allen, *Book of Games for Home, School and Playground*. Philadelphia, John C. Winston Co., 1954.

Gardner, Ella, *Handbook for Recreation Leaders*. Washington, U.S. Government Printing Office, 1936.

Harbin, E. O., *Fun Encyclopedia of Games*. Nashville, Abingdon Press, 1940.

Kraus, Richard, *Play Activities for Boys and Girls*. New York, Mc-Graw-Hill Book Co., Inc., 1957.

Leeming, Joseph, *The Real Book of Games*. Garden City, Doubleday & Co.. Inc., 1953.

Mason, B. S., and E. D. Mitchell, *Social Games for Recreation*. New York, A. S. Barnes & Co., Inc., 1935.

Morehead, A., and G. Mott-Smith, *Hoyle's Rules for Games*. New York, New American Library, 1958.

Ostrow, O. S., *Pastimes for Two*. New York, Harper & Brothers, 1958.

Quinn, Vernon, *50 Card Games for Children*. Cincinnati, U. S. Playing Card Co., 1949.

Rohrbough, Lynn, *Handy Kits*. Delaware, O., Cooperative Recreation Service, n.d.

Sheinwold, Alfred, 101 *Best Card Games for Children*. New York, Sterling Publishing Co., 1956.

Wackerbarth, M., and L. Graham, *Games for All Ages and How to Use Them*. Minneapolis, T. S. Denison & Co., 1958.

Wallace, Carlson, *Treasury of Games and Puzzles*. New York, Philosophical Library, 1958.

Arts and Crafts

Bannon, Laura, *Mind Your Child's Art*. Pellegrini & Cudahy, 1952.

Cane, Florence, *The Artist in Each of Us*. New York, Pantheon Books, Inc., 1951.

Carlson, Bernice, *Make It and Use It*. Nashville, Abingdon Press, 1958.

Cizek, Franz, *Children's Colored Paper Work*. Vienna, Schroll, 1927.

Doan, Eleanore, 201 *Handcrafts for Fun for Little Ones*. Grand Rapids, Zondervan Publishing House, 1955.

Fraser, Grace L., *Doll Making at Home*. New York, Studio Publications, 1944.

Gaba, Lester, *On Soap Sculpturing*. New York, Henry Holt & Co., Inc., 1935.

Gabriel, Sam'l Sons, *Pencil Magic*. New York, Gabriel, 1950.

Hunt, W. Ben, *Golden Book of Indian Crafts and Lore*. New York, Simon and Schuster, Inc., 1954.

Ickis, M., and B. Siks, *The Book of Crafts*. New York, Association Press, 1954.

Jacobs, Frances, *Out of a Handkerchief*. New York, Lothrop, Lee & Shepard Co., Inc., 1942.

Johnson, Pauline, *Creating with Paper*. Seattle, University of Washington Press, 1955.

Lee, Tina, *What to Do Now*. Garden City, Doubleday & Co., Inc., 1946.

Lindstrom, Miriam, *Children's Art*. Berkeley, University of California Press, 1957.

Lowenfeld, Victor, *Your Child and His Art*. New York, The Macmillan Co., 1954.

Martin, Phillip, *Animals for You to Make*. Philadelphia, J. B. Lippincott Co., 1946.

McCall's, *Giant Golden Make-It Book*. New York, Simon & Schuster, Inc., 1953.

Mearns, Hughes, *Creative Power* (2d rev. ed.). New York, Dover Publications, Inc., 1959.

Mendelowitz, Daniel, *Children Are Artists*. Stanford, Stanford University Press, 1956.

Oliver, Rita, *Rain or Shine—Things to Do*. New York, Harcourt, Brace & Co., 1958.

Perrine, Van Dearing, *Let the Child Draw*. New York, Stokes, 1938.

Robertson, Seonaid, *Creative Crafts in Education*. Cambridge, Robert Bentley, Inc., 1953.

Sakade, Florence, *Japanese Paper Folding* (Origami). Rutland, Charles E. Tuttle Co., n.d.

Shaw, Ruth Faison, *Finger Painting and How I Do It*. New York, Leland, 1947.

Wankelman, W., *et al, Arts and Crafts for Elementary Teachers*. Dubuque, William C. Brown Co., 1954.

Dramatics and Puppetry

Berk, Barbara, *The First Book of Stage Costumes and Make Up*. New York, Franklin Watts, Inc., 1954.

Durland, Frances C., *Creative Dramatics for Children*. Yellow Springs, Antioch Press, 1952.

Farnam, Helen, and B. Wheeler, *Let's Make a Puppet*. St. Paul, Webb, 1947.

Ficklen, Bessie, *Handbook of Fist Puppets*. Philadelphia, J. B. Lippincott Co., 1935.

Lease, Ruth G., and G. B. Siks, *Creative Dramatics in Home, School and Community*. New York, Harper & Brothers, 1952.

Leeming, Joseph, *The Costume Book* (7th printing). New York, Stokes, 1943.

Munger, Martha P., and A. L. Elder, *The Book of Puppets*. New York, Lothrop, Lee and Shepard Co., Inc., 1934.

Pels, Gertrude, *Easy Puppets*. New York, Thomas Y. Crowell Co., 1951.

Tichenor, T., *Folk Plays for Puppets*. Nashville, Abingdon Press, 1959.

Wall, L. V. (ed.), *The Complete Puppet Book*. New York, Thomas Y. Crowell Co., 1950.

Ward, Winifred, *Playmaking with Children*. New York, Appleton-Century-Crofts, Inc., 1957.

————, *Stories to Dramatize*. Anchorage, Ky., Children's Theatre Press, 1952.

Literature for Children

Arbuthnot, May Hill, *Children and Books*. New York, The Macmillan Co., 1957.

————, *Time for True Tales*. Chicago, Scott, Foresman & Co., 1953.

Clark, B. H., and M. Jagendorf (eds.), *A World of Stories for Children*. New York, The Bobbs-Merrill Co., Inc., 1947.

Duff, Annis, *Bequest of Wings*. New York, The Viking Press, Inc., 1944.

Eaton, Anne Thaxter, *Treasure for the Taking*. New York, The Viking Press, Inc., 1957.

Fenner, Phyllis, *Something Shared: Children and Books*. New York, The John Day Co., 1959.

————, *The Proof of the Pudding*. New York, The John Day Co., 1956.

————, *What Children Read*. New York, The John Day Co., 1957.

Frank, Josette, *Your Child's Reading Today*. Garden City, Doubleday & Co., Inc., 1954.

Greenberg, Sidonie M., *Favorite Stories Old and New* (rev. ed.). Garden City, Doubleday & Co., Inc., 1942.

Huber, Miriam B., *Story and Verse for Children*. New York, The Macmillan Co., 1955.

Martignoni, Margaret, *Illustrated Treasury of Children's Literature*. Dunlap, 1955.

Mitchell, Lucy S., *Here and Now Story Book*. New York, E. P. Dutton & Co., Inc., 1948.

Sawyer, Ruth, *The Way of the Storyteller*. New York, The Viking Press, Inc., 1942.

Shedlock, Marie, *The Art of the Story Teller*. New York, Dover Publications, Inc., 1951.

Tooze, Ruth, *Storytelling*. Englewood Cliffs, Prentice-Hall, Inc., 1959.

Music, Songs, and Singing Games

Andrews, Gladys, *Creative Rhythmic Movements for Children*. Englewood Cliffs, Prentice-Hall, Inc., 1954.

Bley, Edgar S., *Best Singing Games*. New York, Sterling Publishing Co., Inc., 1957.

Boni, Margaret B., *Fireside Book of Folk Songs*. New York, Simon & Schuster, Inc., 1952.

Botsford, Florence, *Universal Folk Songster*. New York, G. Schirmer, Inc., 1937.

Botwin, Esther, *A Treasury of Songs for Little Children*. New York, Hart Publishing Co., 1952.

Boyd, Neva L., and D. Pedersen, *Folk Games and Gymnastic Play*. Chicago, FitzSimons, 1932.

————, *Folk Games of Denmark and Sweden*. Chicago, FitzSimons, 1932.

Boyd, Neva L., and F. W. Brown, *Old English and American Games*. Chicago, FitzSimons, 1932.

Coleman, Satis, *Creative Music in the Home*. New York, The John Day Co., 1939.

————, *Dancing Time*. New York, The John Day Co., 1952.

————, *Singing Time* (new ed.). New York, The John Day Co., 1950.

————, and A. Bergman, *Songs of American Folk*. New York, The John Day Co., 1952.

Commins, Dorothy B., *Big Book of Favorite Songs*. Dunlap, 1951.

Kapp, Paul, *A Cat Came Fiddling*. New York, Harcourt, Brace & Co., 1956.

Landeck, Beatrice, *Children and Music*. New York, William Sloane Associates, 1952.

————, *Songs to Grow On*. New York, Marks, Sloane, 1950.

————, *More Songs to Grow On*. New York, Marks, Sloane, 1954.

Lomax, J., and A. Lomax, *Best Loved American Folk Songs*. New York, Grosset & Dunlap, Inc., 1947.

————, *Cowboy Songs and Other Frontier Ballads*. New York, The Macmillan Co., 1946.

Ohanian, Phyllis, *Favorite Nursery Songs*. New York, Random House, 1956.

Ritchey, Jean, *Swapping Song Book*. New York, Oxford University Press, 1952.

Schullian, Dorothy, and Max Schoen, *Music and Medicine*. New York, Schuman, 1948.

Seeger, Ruth, *American Folk Songs for Children*. New York, Doubleday & Co., Inc., 1948.

————, *Animal Folk Songs for Children*. New York, Doubleday & Co., Inc., 1950.

Wall, Willem van de, *Music in Institutions*. New York, Russell Sage Foundation, 1936.

Young, Percy, and E. Ardizzone, *Ding Dong Bell*. London, Dobson, 1957.

Zanzig, Augustus, *Singing America*. Boston, Birchard, 1941.

Poetry, Nonsense Rhymes, and Riddles

Aldis, Dorothy, *All Together*. New York, G. P. Putnam's Sons, 1952.

Association of Childhood Education, *Sung Under the Silver Umbrella*. New York, The Macmillan Co., 1947.

Becker, John, *New Feathers for the Old Goose*. New York, Pantheon Books, Inc., 1956.

Carlson, G. L., 1001 *Riddles for Children*. New York, Platt & Munk Co., Inc., 1949.

Cole, William, *Humorous Poetry for Children*. Cleveland, World, 1955.

Crystie, Frances, *Riddle Me This*. New York, Oxford University Press, 1940.

De La Mare, Walter, *Peacock Pie* (new ed.). New York, Henry Holt & Co., Inc., 1957.

Eastman, Max, *Enjoyment of Poetry*. New York, Charles Scribner's Sons, 1951.

Justus, May, *Pedlar's Pack*. New York, Henry Holt & Co., Inc., 1957.

Lear, Edward, *Complete Nonsense Book*. New York, Dodd, Mead & Co., 1956.

Leeming, Joseph, *Riddles, Riddles, Riddles*. New York, Franklin Watts, Inc., 1953.

MacFarland, Wilma K., *For a Child: Great Poems Old and New*. Philadelphia, Westminster Press, 1957.

Mellon, Robert C., *Super Duper Riddles*. New York, Hart Publishing Co., 1958.

Morrison, Lillian, *A Dillar a Dollar*. New York, Thomas Y. Crowell Co., 1955.

Richards, Laura E., *Tirra Lirra; Rhymes Old and New*. Boston, Little Brown & Co., 1955.

Rossetti, Christina, *Sing Song* (new ed.). New York, The Macmillan Co., 1952.

Salaff, Alice, *Words Are Funny*. New York, Doubleday & Co., Inc., 1952.

Smith, Janet A., *Faber Book of Children's Verse*. London, Faber, 1954.

Stevenson, Robert, *A Child's Garden of Verses*. New York, Grosset & Dunlap, Inc., 1957.

Withers, Carl, *A Rocket in My Pocket*. New York, Henry Holt & Co., Inc., 1948.

————, and Sula Benet, *American Riddle Book*. New York, Abelard-Schuman, Ltd., 1954.

————, *Riddles of Many Lands*. New York, Abelard-Schuman, Ltd., 1956.

Child Care and Development

Adler, Alfred, *The Education of Children*. New York, Greenberg: Publisher, 1930.

Aldrich, C. A., and M. M. Aldrich, *Babies Are Human Beings*. New York, The Macmillan Co., 1954.

Anderson, Harold, *Children in the Family*. New York, Appleton-Century-Crofts, Inc., 1954.

Baruch, Dorothy, *New Ways in Discipline*. New York, Whittlesey House, 1949.

Bauer, W. W., M.D., *Stop Annoying Your Children*. New York, The Bobbs-Merrill Co., Inc., 1947.

Buckley, I. P., *Guide to a Child's World*. New York, Henry Holt & Co., Inc., 1951.

Child Study Association of America, *Guidance of Childhood and Youth*. New York, The Macmillan Co., 1949.

Cooperative Parents, *The Challenge of Children*. Whiteside-Morrison, 1957.

Dixon, C. M., *Keep Them Human*. New York, The John Day Co., 1942.

Dunbar, H. Flanders, *Your Child's Mind and Body* (3d ed.). New York, Random House, 1955.

Faegre, M. L., *et al, Child Care and Training* (8th rev. ed.). Minneapolis, Minnesota University Press, 1958.

Gesell, A., and F. Ilg, *Infant and Child in the Culture of Today*. New York, Harper & Brothers, 1949.

Hartley, Ruth, *et al, Complete Book of Children's Play*. New York, Thomas Y. Crowell Co., 1957.

————, *Understanding Children's Play*. New York, Columbia University Press, 1952.

Homan, Leslie B., *As the Twig Is Bent*. New York, The Macmillan Co., 1943.

Hymes, James L., *Understanding Your Child*. Englewood Cliffs, Prentice-Hall, Inc., 1957.

Kugelmass, Newton, *Complete Child Care in Body and Mind*. New York, Twayne Publishers, 1960.

Lane, H., and Mary Beauchamp, *Understanding Human Development*. Englewood Cliffs, Prentice-Hall, Inc., 1959.

Moustakas, Clark E., *Children in Play Therapy*. New York, McGraw-Hill Book Co., Inc., 1953.

Pratt, Caroline, *I Learn from Children*. New York, Simon and Schuster, Inc., 1948.

Reynolds, Martha, *Children from Seeds to Saplings*. New York, McGraw-Hill Book Co., 1951.

Seipt, Irene S., *Your Child's Happiness*. World, 1955.

Those Who Are Different

Apton, Adolph, M.D., *The Handicapped: A Challenge to the Non-Handicapped*. New York, Citadel Press, 1959.

Baker, Louise, *Out on a Limb*. New York, Whittlesey House, 1946.

Barton, Betsy, *And Now to Live Again*. New York, Appleton-Century-Crofts, Inc., 1955.

Brown, Audrey, *Log of a Lame Duck*. New York, The Macmillan Co., 1939.

Bruckner, Leona S., *Triumph of Love*. New York, Simon and Schuster, Inc., 1954.

Buck, Pearl, *The Child That Never Grew*. New York, The John Day Co., 1930.

Culbertson, Polly, *Kindergarten in the Kitchen*. Dunlap, 1954.

Field, Minna, *Patients Are People* (2d ed.). New York, Columbia University Press, 1958.

Forney, Katherine, *Up and Away*. New York, Exposition Press, Inc., 1957.

Frank, John P., *My Son's Story*. New York, Alfred A. Knopf, Inc., 1951.

Heiser, Karl F., *Our Backward Children*. New York, W. W. Norton & Co., 1955.

Hood, O. E., *Your Child or Mine*. New York, Harper & Brothers, 1957.

Hutt, Max, and R. Gibby, *The Mentally Retarded Child*. Boston, Allyn & Bacon, Inc., 1958.

Kessler, Henry, *Rehabilitation of the Physically Handicapped* (rev. ed.). New York, Columbia University Press, 1953.

Ketcham, Dorothy, *One Hundred Thousand Days of Illness*. Ann Arbor, J. W. Edwards, Publisher, Inc., 1939.

Killilea, M., *Karen*. Englewood Cliffs, Prentice-Hall, Inc., 1953.

Kirk, Samuel, *et al, You and Your Retarded Child*. New York, The Macmillan Co., 1955.

Levinson, Abe, *The Mentally Retarded Child*. New York, The John Day Co., 1952.

Loewy, Herta, *The Retarded Child*. New York, Philosophical Library, Inc., 1951.

Lewis, R. *et al, The Other Child*. New York, Grune & Stratton, Inc., 1953.

Mallison, Vernon, *None Can Be Called Deformed*. New York, W. S. Heinman, 1956.

Masland, R., *et al, Mental Subnormality*. New York, Basic Books, Inc., 1958.

Schlotter B., and M. Svendsen, *An Experiment in Recreation with the Mentally Retarded*. National Mental Health, 1951.

Stern, E. M., and E. Castendyck, *The Handicapped Child, A Guide to Parents*. New York, A. A. Wyn, Inc., 1950.

INDEX